Christopher M. Langan

The Cognitive-Theoretic Model of the Universe:
A New Kind of Reality Theory

Mega Foundation Press

First Published in 2002

www.ctmu.org

www.patreon.com/CTMU

This New Edition 2020

Published by
Mega Foundation Press, Inc.
PO Box 111
Princeton, MO 64673

info@megapress.org

Langan, C. M. (Christopher Michael)

The Cognitive-Theoretic Model of the Universe:
A New Kind of Reality Theory

1. Metaphysics 2. General Knowledge

ISBN 978-0-9719162-2-7

Contents

Diagrams

Abstract

Inasmuch as science is observational or perceptual in nature, the goal of providing a scientific model and mechanism for the evolution of complex systems ultimately requires a supporting theory of reality of which perception itself is the model (or theory-to-universe mapping). Where *information* is the abstract currency of perception, such a theory must incorporate the theory of information while extending the information concept to incorporate reflexive self-processing in order to achieve an intrinsic (self-contained) description of reality. This extension is associated with a limiting formulation of model theory identifying mental and physical reality, resulting in a reflexively self-generating, self-modeling theory of reality identical to its universe on the syntactic level. By the nature of its derivation, this theory, the *Cognitive Theoretic Model of the Universe* or CTMU, can be regarded as a *supertautological* reality-theoretic extension of logic. Uniting the theory of reality with an advanced form of computational language theory, the CTMU describes reality as a *Self-Configuring Self-Processing Language* or SCSPL, a reflexive *intrinsic language* characterized not only by self-reference and recursive self-definition, but full self-configuration and self-execution (reflexive read-write functionality). SCSPL reality embodies a dual-aspect monism consisting of *infocognition*, self-transducing information residing in self-recognizing SCSPL elements called *syntactic operators*. The CTMU identifies itself with the structure of these operators and thus with the distributive syntax of its self-modeling SCSPL universe, including the reflexive grammar by which the universe refines itself from *unbound telesis* or UBT, a primordial realm of infocognitive potential free of informational constraint. Under the guidance of a limiting (intrinsic) form of anthropic principle called the *Telic Principle*, SCSPL evolves by *telic recursion*, jointly configuring syntax and state while maximizing a generalized self-selection parameter and adjusting on the fly to freely-changing internal conditions. SCSPL relates *space, time* and *object* by means of *conspansive duality* and *conspansion*, an SCSPL-grammatical process featuring an alternation between dual phases of existence associated with design and actualization and related to the familiar wave-particle duality of quantum mechanics. By distributing the design phase of reality over the actualization phase, conspansive spacetime also provides a distributed mechanism for *Intelligent Design*, adjoining to the restrictive principle of natural selection a basic means of generating information and complexity. Addressing physical evolution on not only the biological but cosmic level, the CTMU addresses the most evident deficiencies and paradoxes associated with conventional discrete and continuum models of reality, including temporal directionality and accelerating cosmic expansion, while preserving virtually all of the major benefits of current scientific and mathematical paradigms.

1

1 Introduction

Among the most exciting recent developments in science are *Complexity Theory*, the theory of self-organizing systems, and the modern incarnation of *Intelligent Design Theory*, which investigates the deep relationship between self-organization and evolutionary biology in a scientific context not preemptively closed to teleological causation. Bucking the traditional physical reductionism of the hard sciences, complexity theory has given rise to a new trend, *informational reductionism*, which holds that the basis of reality is not matter and energy, but information. Unfortunately, this new form of reductionism is as problematic as the old one. As mathematician David Berlinski (2001) writes regarding the material and informational aspects of DNA: "We quite know what DNA is: it is a macromolecule and so a material object. We quite know what it achieves: apparently everything. Are the two sides of this equation in balance?" More generally, Berlinski observes that since the information embodied in a string of DNA or protein cannot affect the material dynamic of reality without being read by a material transducer, information is meaningless without matter.

The relationship between physical and informational reductionism is a telling one, for it directly mirrors Cartesian *mind-matter dualism*, the source of several centuries of philosophical and scientific controversy regarding the nature of deep reality (Wozniak, 1992). As long as matter and information remain separate, with specialists treating one as primary while tacitly relegating the other to secondary status, dualism remains in effect. To this extent, history is merely repeating itself; where mind and matter once vied with each other for primary status, concrete matter now vies with abstract information *abstractly representing* matter and its extended relationships. But while the formal abstractness and concrete descriptiveness of information seem to make it a worthy compromise between mind and matter, Berlinski's comment demonstrates its inadequacy as a conceptual substitute. What is now required is thus what has been required all along: a conceptual framework in which the relationship between mind and matter, cognition and information, is made explicit. This framework must not only permit the completion of the gradual ongoing dissolution of the Cartesian mind-matter divider, but the construction of a footworthy logical bridge across the resulting explanatory gap.

Mathematically, the theoretical framework of Intelligent Design consists of certain definitive principles governing the application of complexity and probability to the analysis of two key attributes of evolutionary phenomena, *irreducible complexity* (Behe, 1998) and *specified complexity* (Dembski, 1998). On one hand, because the mathematics of probability must be causally interpreted to be scientifically meaningful, and because probabilities are therefore expressly relativized to specific causal scenarios, it is difficult to assign definite probabilities to evolutionary states in any model not supporting the detailed reconstruction and analysis of specific causal pathways. On the other hand, positing the "absolute improbability" of an evolutionary state ultimately entails the specification of an absolute (intrinsic global) model with respect to which absolute probabilistic deviations can be determined. A little reflection suffices to inform us of some of its properties: it must be rationally derivable from *a priori* principles and essentially tautological in nature, it must on some level identify matter and information, and it must eliminate the explanatory gap between the mental and physical aspects of reality. Furthermore, in keeping with the name of that to be modeled, it must meaningfully incorporate the *intelligence* and *design* concepts, describing the universe as an intelligently self-designed, self-organizing system.

How is this to be done? In a word, with *language*. This does not mean merely that language should be used as a tool to analyze reality, for this has already been done countless times with varying degrees of success. Nor does it mean that reality should be regarded as a machine language running in some kind of vast computer. It means using language as a *mathematical paradigm unto itself.* Of all mathematical structures, language is the most general, powerful and necessary. Not only is every formal or working theory of science and mathematics by definition a language, but science and mathematics in whole and in sum are languages. Everything that can be described or conceived, including every structure or process or law, is isomorphic to a description or definition and therefore qualifies as a language, and every sentient creature constantly affirms the linguistic structure of nature by exploiting syntactic isomorphism to perceive, conceptualize and refer to it. Even cognition and perception are languages based on what Kant might have called "phenomenal syntax". With logic and mathematics counted among its most fundamental syntactic ingredients, language defines the very structure of information. This is more than an empirical truth; it is a rational and scientific necessity.

Of particular interest to natural scientists is the fact that the laws of nature are a language. To some extent, nature is regular; the basic patterns or general aspects of structure in terms of which it is apprehended, whether or not they have been categorically identified, are its "laws". The existence of these laws is given by the stability of perception. Because these repetitive patterns or universal laws simultaneously describe multiple instances or states of nature, they can be regarded as distributed "instructions" from which self-instantiations of nature cannot deviate; thus, they form a "control language" through which nature regulates its self-instantiations. This control language is not of the usual kind, for it is somehow built into the very fabric of reality and seems to override the known limitations of formal systems. Moreover, it is profoundly reflexive and self-contained with respect to configuration, execution and read-write operations. Only the few and the daring have been willing to consider how this might work . . . to ask where in reality the laws might reside, how they might be expressed and implemented, why and how they came to be, and how their consistency and universality are maintained. Although these questions are clearly of great scientific interest, science alone is logically inadequate to answer them; a new explanatory framework is required. This paper describes what the author considers to be the most promising framework in the simplest and most direct terms possible.

On a note of forbearance, there has always been comfort in the belief that the standard hybrid empirical-mathematical methods of physics and cosmology will ultimately suffice to reveal the true heart of nature. However, there have been numerous signals that it may be time to try a new approach. With true believers undaunted by the (mathematically factual) explanatory limitations of the old methods, we must of course empathize; it is hard to question one's prior investments when one has already invested all the faith that one has. But science and philosophy do not progress by regarding their past investments as ends in themselves; the object is always to preserve that which is valuable in the old methods while adjoining new methods that refine their meaning and extend their horizons. The new approach that we will be exploring in this paper, which might be colorfully rendered as "reality theory is wedded to language theory and they beget a synthesis", has the advantage that it leaves the current picture of reality virtually intact. It merely creates a logical mirror image of the current picture (its *conspansive dual*), merges the symmetric halves of the resulting picture, and attempts to extract meaningful implications. Science as we now know it is thereby changed but little in return for what may, if fate smiles upon us, turn out to be vast gains in depth, significance and explanatory power.

And on that note, I thank you for your kind attention and wish you a fruitful journey.

2 On Theories, Models and False Dichotomies

It has almost become embarrassing to point out that science is in a state of crisis ... not because it is untrue, but because it has become a *cliché* too often accompanied by little or no remedial insight. For all of the magnificent achievements of science, its grander ambitions long ago succeeded in taxing its traditional models and organizational principles beyond their explanatory limits. In the search for ever deeper and broader explanations, science has reached the point at which it can no longer deny the existence of intractable conceptual difficulties devolving to the explanatory inadequacies of its fundamental conceptual models of reality. This has spawned a new discipline known as *reality theory*, the study of the nature of reality in its broadest sense. The overall goal of reality theory is to provide new models and new paradigms in terms of which reality can be understood, and the consistency of science restored as it deepens and expands in scope.

Mainstream reality theory counts among its hotter foci the interpretation of quantum theory and its reconciliation with classical physics, the study of subjective consciousness and its relationship to objective material reality, the reconciliation of science and mathematics, complexity theory, cosmology, and related branches of science, mathematics, philosophy and theology. But in an integrated sense, it is currently in an exploratory mode, being occupied with the search for a general conceptual framework in which to develop a more specific theory and model of reality capable of resolving the paradoxes and conceptual inconsistencies plaguing its various fields of interest (where a *model* is technically defined as a valid interpretation of a theory in its universe of reference). Because of the universal scope of reality theory, it is subject to unique if seldom-recognized demands; for example, since it is by definition a universal theory of everything that is real, it must by definition contain its rules of real-world interpretation. That is, reality theory must contain its own model and effect its own self-interpretative mapping thereto, and it must conform to the implications of this requirement. This "self-modeling" capacity is a primary criterion of the required framework.

The ranks of reality theorists include researchers from almost every scientific discipline. As the physical sciences have become more invested in a quantum mechanical view of reality, and as science in general has become more enamored of and dependent on computer simulation as an experimental tool, the traditional continuum model of classical physics has gradually lost ground to a new class of models to which the concepts of information and computation are essential. Called "discrete models", they depict reality in terms of bits, quanta, quantum events, computational operations and other discrete, recursively-related units. Whereas continuum models are based on the notion of a *continuum*, a unified extensible whole with one or more distance parameters that can be infinitely subdivided in such a way that any two distinct points are separated by an infinite number of intermediate points, discrete models are distinguished by realistic acknowledgement of the fact that it is impossible to describe or define a change or separation in any way that does not involve a sudden finite jump in some parameter.

Unfortunately, the advantages of discrete models, which are receiving increasingly serious consideration from the scientific and philosophical communities, are outweighed by certain basic deficiencies. Not only do they exhibit scaling and nonlocality problems associated with their "display hardware", but they are inadequate by themselves to generate the conceptual infrastructure required to explain the medium, device or array in which they evolve, or their initial states and state-transition programming. Moreover, they remain anchored in materialism, objectivism and Cartesian dualism, each of which has proven obstructive to the development of a comprehensive explanation of reality. Materialism arbitrarily excludes the possibility that reality has a meaningful nonmaterial aspect, objectivism arbitrarily excludes the possibility that reality has a meaningful subjective aspect, and although Cartesian dualism technically excludes neither, it arbitrarily denies that the mental and material, or subjective and objective, sides of reality share common substance.[1]

One might almost get the impression that the only two available choices are the classical model, to which quantum theory has been fastened with approximately the same degree of cogency as antlers on a jackrabbit, and the newer discrete models, which purport to be more in line with quantum theory but fall by the wayside *en route* to the new kind of quantum cosmology they portentously seem to promise. For such claims exhibit an unmistakable irony: classical reality is precisely that on which information and computation are defined! Like classical reality itself, a well-defined entity unable to account for its own genesis, information and computation are well-defined and non-self-generative aspects of reality as it is observationally presented to us at an advanced stage of its existence. So they invite the same questions as does classical reality: how, and by what, were they originally defined and generated? Without an answer to this question, little can be gained by replacing one kind of reality with the other.

Some may have felt, as they watched the history of Big Theories and New Paradigms unfold over the last few years, as though they were being forced to watch the same show, or read the same novel, a thousand times in tedious succession with no more than an occasional minor revision of plot or character. However, there is a third alternative which has thus far remained in the background. It provides exactly what is required in light of any thesis and antithesis: synthesis. This synthesis yields a new class of model(s)[2] preserving the best features of both thesis and antithesis, continuum and

---

[1] In fact, they are identical up to an isomorphism beyond which the mental side, being the more comprehensive of the two, outstrips the material.

[2] Although the CTMU is by definition unique up to isomorphism with its own syntax – this "self-isomorphism" is one of its definitive structural characteristics – we will duly refrain from summarily ruling out the possibility that in the future, others may present self-determinative "temporal feedback models" of their

quantum, uniting them through general and preferably self-evident principles. This paper presents this new class through a single example, the *Cognitive-Theoretic Model of the Universe* (CTMU).

own. It should be noted, however, that since the CTMU is intrinsically tautological and tautologically identified with its universe on the deepest level of its existence, and since this is the selfsame real universe studied by science, any other valid theory of reality will necessarily equate to the CTMU up to isomorphism; whatever it adds will come by way of specificity, not generality. Although others have already presented "cybernetic" and "information-theoretic" theories of cosmology, these theories rely on the standard theories of information and cybernetics, and thus inherit their explanatory limitations with respect to cosmology.

3 Determinacy, Indeterminacy and the Third Option

Like the mathematics, science and philosophy whence they issue, classical continuum and modern discrete models of reality generally allow for exactly two modes of determinacy: external causality, and acausality or "randomness". Given an object, event, set or process, it is usually assumed to have come about in one or both of just two ways:

(1)   its existence owes to something prior and external to it;

(2)   it is uncaused and sprang forth spontaneously and pointlessly in a something-from-nothing, rabbit-out-of-the-hat sort of way, as if by magic.

A similar assumption is made with regard to its behavior: either it is controlled by laws that are invariant with respect to it and therefore existentially external to it (even though they control it through its intrinsic structure and properties), or it is behaving in an utterly aleatory and uncontrolled fashion. This has given rise to a dichotomy: *determinacy versus randomness*, or a total absence of causation versus causation by laws that are ultimately independent of the determined entity.

Determinacy and indeterminacy . . . at first glance, there seems to be no middle ground. Events are either causally connected or they are not, and if they are not, then the future would seem to be utterly independent of the past. Either we use causality to connect the dots and draw a coherent picture of time, or we settle for a random scattering of independent dots without spatial or temporal pattern and thus without meaning. At the risk of understatement, the philosophical effects of this assumed dichotomy have been corrosive in the extreme. No universe that exists or evolves strictly as a function of external determinacy, randomness or an alternation of the two can offer much in the way of meaning. Where freedom and volition are irrelevant, so is much of human experience and individuality.

But there is another possibility after all: *self-determinacy*. Self-determinacy is like a circuitous boundary separating the poles of the above dichotomy . . . a reflexive and therefore closed boundary, the formation of which involves neither preexisting laws nor external structure. Thus, it is the type of causal attribution suitable for a perfectly self-contained system. Self-determinacy is a deep but subtle concept, owing largely to the fact that unlike either determinacy or randomness, it is a source of *bona fide* meaning. Where a system determines its own composition, properties and evolution independently of external laws or structures, it can determine its *own* meaning, and ensure by its self-configuration that its inhabitants are crucially implicated therein.

If determinacy corresponds to an arrow of causation pointing to an event from a surrounding medium, then indeterminacy corresponds to no arrow at all (acausality), and self-determinacy to a looping arrow or complex of arrows involving some kind of feedback. But cybernetic feedback, which involves information passed among controllers

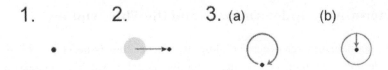

DIAGRAM I 1. *Indeterminacy* 2. *External determinacy* 3a. *Self-determinacy* 3b. *Intrinsic self-determinacy*: The effectual aspect of the object or event has simply been moved inside the causal aspect, permitting the internalization of the blue arrow of determinacy and making causality *endomorphic.*

and regulated entities through a conductive or transmissive medium, is meaningless where such entities do not already exist, and where no sensory or actuative protocol has yet been provided. With respect to the origin of any self-determinative, perfectly self-contained system, the feedback is ontological in nature and therefore more than cybernetic. Accordingly, ontological feedback bears description as "precybernetic" or "metacybernetic". Indeed, because of their particularly close relationship, the theories of information, computation and cybernetics are all in line for a convergent extension . . . an extension that can, in a reality-theoretic context, lay much of the groundwork for a convergent extension of all that is covered by their respective formalisms.[3]

Ordinary feedback, describing the evolution of mechanical (and with somewhat less success, biological) systems, is cyclical or recursive. The system and its components repeatedly call on internal structures, routines and actuation mechanisms in order to acquire input, generate corresponding internal information, internally communicate and process this information, and evolve to appropriate states in light of input and programming. However, where the object is to describe the evolution of a system from a state in which there is no information or programming (information-processing syntax) at all, a new kind of feedback is required: *telic feedback.*

The currency of telic feedback is a quantifiable self-selection parameter, *generalized utility*, a generalized property of law and state in the maximization of which they undergo mutual refinement (note that generalized utility is self-descriptive or *autologous*, intrinsically and retroactively defined within the system, and "pre-informational" in the sense that it assigns no specific property to any specific object). Through telic feedback, a system retroactively self-configures by reflexively applying a "generalized utility function" to its internal existential potential or possible futures. In effect, the system brings itself into existence as a means of atemporal communication between its past and future whereby law and state, syntax and informational content, generate and refine each other across time to maximize total systemic self-utility. This defines

---

[3] Those who expect the field of cosmology to culminate in a grand reduction of the universe to pure information sometimes forget that this would merely transform a certain question, "what is the universe and where did it come from?", to another no less vexing question, "what is information and where did it come from?"

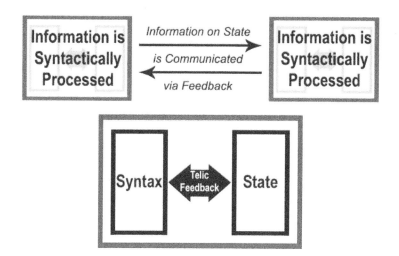

DIAGRAM II The upper diagram illustrates ordinary cybernetic feedback between two information transducers exchanging and acting on information reflecting their internal states. The structure and behavior of each transducer conforms to a *syntax*, or set of structural and functional rules which determine how it behaves on a given input. To the extent that each transducer is either deterministic or nondeterministic (within the bounds of syntactic constraint), the system is either deterministic or "random up to determinacy"; there is no provision for self-causation below the systemic level. The lower diagram, which applies to coherent self-designing systems, illustrates a situation in which syntax and state are instead determined in tandem according to a generalized utility function assigning differential but intrinsically-scaled values to various possible syntax-state relationships. A combination of these two scenarios is partially illustrated in the upper diagram by the gray shadows within each transducer.

a situation in which the true temporal identity of the system is a distributed point of temporal equilibrium that is both *between* and *inclusive* of past and future. In this sense, the system is timeless or *atemporal*.

A system that evolves by means of telic recursion – and ultimately, every system must either be, or be embedded in, such a system as a condition of existence – is not merely computational, but *protocomputational*. That is, its primary level of processing configures its secondary (computational and informational) level of processing by telic recursion. Telic recursion can be regarded as the self-determinative mechanism of not only cosmogony, but a natural, scientific form of teleology.

However, before taking these ideas any further, let's attend a little orientation session based on the remarkably penetrating vision of John Archibald Wheeler, a preeminent scientist and reality theorist whose name is virtually synonymous with modern physics.

4 The Future of Reality Theory According to John Wheeler

In 1979, the celebrated physicist John Wheeler, having coined the phrase "black hole", put it to good philosophical use in the title of an exploratory paper, "Beyond the Black Hole" (1980), in which he describes the universe as a *self-excited circuit*. The paper includes an illustration in which one side of an uppercase U, ostensibly standing for *Universe*, is endowed with a large and rather intelligent-looking eye intently regarding the other side, which it ostensibly acquires through observation as sensory information. By dint of placement, the eye stands for the sensory or *cognitive* aspect of reality, perhaps even a human spectator within the universe, while the eye's perceptual target represents the *informational* aspect of reality. By virtue of these complementary aspects, it seems that the universe can in some sense, but not necessarily that of common usage, be described as "conscious" and "introspective" . . . perhaps even "infocognitive".

DIAGRAM III The Universe as a self-excited circuit. Diagram adapted from Wheeler, J. A. (1980).

Wheeler, an eminent and highly capable representative of those familiar with the advantages and deficiencies of our current models of reality, did not arrive at the given illustration as an isolated speculation. In conjunction with several other Wheeler concepts, the *Participatory Universe, Law without Law* and *It from Bit*, the self-excited circuit amounts to a preliminary but well-considered program for describing the physical universe. According to its mandate, the true description of reality must possess two novel features not found in any dominant paradigm:

(1) *global structural and dynamical reflexivity* or "self-excited circuitry", with perception an integral part of the self-recognition function of reality;

(2) *matter-information equivalence*, an identification (up to isomorphism) of concrete physical reality with information, the abstract currency of perception.

Together, these features constitute a cosmological extension of cybernetics, or equivalently, a metacybernetic extension of cosmology.

Wheeler characterizes these four concepts as follows:

The Self-Excited Circuit A participatory universe is a self-excited circuit in the sense that it implicates observers in (perceptual, ontological) feedback. It is a "logic loop" in which "physics gives rise to observer-participancy; observer-participancy gives rise to information; and information gives rise to physics" (1990a, p. 8).

The Participatory Universe The cognitive and perceptual processes of observers are integral to the self-excitative feedback of reality. This is asserted by the *Participatory Principle* (or *Participatory Anthropic Principle*), which Wheeler (1979) informally describes as follows:

> Stronger than the Anthropic Principle is what I might call the *Participatory Principle*. According to it, we could not even imagine a universe that did not somewhere and for some stretch of time contain observers, because the very building materials of the universe are these acts of observer-participancy. ... This participatory principle takes for its foundation the absolutely central point of the quantum: no elementary phenomenon is a phenomenon until it is an *observed* (or registered) phenomenon [emphasis added].

Note that on some level of generality, the last sentence identifies observation with registration and thus implicitly equates human and mechanical recognition: ". . . an observed (or *registered*) phenomenon" [emphasis again added].

Law Without Law / Order from Disorder Concisely, nothing can be taken as given when it comes to cosmogony. In Professor Wheeler's (1979) own words:

> To me, the greatest discovery yet to come will be to find how this universe, coming into being from a Big Bang, developed its laws of operation. I call this "Law without Law" [or "Order from Disorder"]. ... imagine the universe with all its regularities and its laws coming into being out of something utterly helter-skelter, higgledy-piggledy and random ... If you were the Lord constructing the universe, how would you have gone about it? It's inspiring to read the life of Charles Darwin and think how the division of plant and animal kingdoms, all this myriad of order, came about through the miracles of evolution, natural selection and chance mutation. To me this is a marvelous indication that you can get order by starting with disorder.

It From Bit Reality educes and/or produces itself in the form of information residing in quantum events. As Wheeler summarizes in his paper "Information, Physics, Quantum: The Search for Links" (1990a, p. 3-4): ". . . every physical quantity, every it, derives its ultimate significance from bits, binary yes-or-no indications . . ." He then goes on to discuss this concept at length, offering three questions, four "no's" and five "clues" about the quantum-informational character of reality. The questions are as follows: (1) *How come existence?* (2) *How come the quantum?* (3) *How come the "one* *world" out of many observer-participants?* The no's, seductive pitfalls to be avoided in answering the three questions, include *No tower of turtles, No laws, No continuum,* and *No space, no time.* And the clues, which light the way toward the true answers, include *The boundary of a boundary is zero; No question? No answer!; The Super-Copernican Principle; "Consciousness"* (including the quotes); and *More is different.*

We will now give a brief account of these questions, precautions and clues.[4]

How come existence? The ontological and cosmological thrust of this question is obvious; in some form, it has bedeviled philosophers from time immemorial. As interpreted by Wheeler, it leads to four inevitable conclusions:

> (1) The world cannot be a giant machine, ruled by any pre-established continuum physical law. (2) There is no such thing at the microscopic level as space or time or spacetime continuum. (3) The familiar probability function or functional, and wave equation or functional wave equation, of standard quantum theory provide mere continuum idealizations and by reason of this circumstance conceal the information-theoretic source from which they derive. (4) No element in the description of physics shows itself as closer to primordial than the elementary quantum phenomenon, that is, the elementary device-intermediated act of posing a yes-no physical question and eliciting an answer or, in brief, the elementary act of observer-participancy. Otherwise stated, every physical quantity, every it, derives its ultimate significance from bits, binary yes-or-no indications, a conclusion which we epitomize in the phrase, *it from bit.*

How come the quantum? Why is the universe made up of apparently *propter hoc* nondeterministic, but *post hoc* informational, quantum events? As Wheeler observes: "Quantum physics requires a new view of reality." What, then, is the exact logical relationship between the quantum and the new view of reality it demands? What is this new view, and how does the quantum fit into it?

How come the "one world" out of many observer-participants? Insofar as the term "observer-participants" embraces scientists and other human beings, this question invites a quasi-anthropological interpretation. Why should a universe consisting of separate observers with sometimes conflicting agendas and survival imperatives display structural and nomological unity? Where observers are capable of creating events within the global unitary manifold of their common universe, why should they not be doing it strictly for themselves, each in his or her *own* universe, and never the twain shall meet? Where the observer-participant concept is generalized to include non-anthropic information-transducing systems, what is holding all of these systems together in a single unified reality?

---

[4] Unless stated otherwise, the Wheeler quotes are from the 1990a article mentioned above.

No tower of turtles Borrowed from William James, this aphorism means "no infinite regress to ever-prior causal domains and principles". To this we might equate an updated version of a well-known aphorism credited to Harry Truman: "The explanatory buck stops here", where *here* refers to this reality that we actually inhabit and observe. To this Wheeler adds a crucial insight: "To endlessness no alternative is evident but loop, such a loop as this: Physics gives rise to observer-participancy; observer-participancy gives rise to information; and information gives rise to physics."

No laws Wheeler states that the universe must have come into being without "a pre-existing plan . . . Only a principle of organization which is no organization at all would seem to offer itself". Or to reiterate: "The world cannot be a giant machine, ruled by any pre-established continuum physical law."

No continuum The venerable continuum of analysis and mechanics is a mathematical and physical chimera. (Usually associated with the set of real numbers, a *continuum* is a unified extensible whole with a distance parameter that can be infinitely subdivided in such a way that any two distinct points are separated by an infinite number of intermediate points.) As Wheeler puts it: "A half-century of development in the sphere of mathematical logic has made it clear that there is no evidence supporting the belief in the existential character of the number continuum." Some numbers, e.g. irrational ones like $\sqrt{2}$, cannot be precisely computed and therefore do not correspond to any physically meaningful location on a number line or physical trajectory; they have an abstract existence only.

No space, no time Again, "there is no such thing at the microscopic level as space or time or spacetime continuum." On the the submicroscopic level, the Heisenberg Uncertainty Principle turns spacetime into seemingly chaotic "quantum foam", casting doubt on the connectivity of space and the ordinality of time. Wheeler quotes Einstein in a Kantian vein: 'Time and space are modes by which we think, and not conditions in which we live', regarding these modes as derivable from a proper theory of reality as idealized functions of an idealized continuum: "We will not feed time into any deep-reaching account of existence. We must derive time – and time only in the continuum idealization – out of it. Likewise with space."

The boundary of a boundary is zero In essence, this intuitive notion from algebraic topology says that closed structures embody a certain kind of "self-cancellative" symmetry. This can be illustrated in three dimensions by a tetrahedron, the simplicial "boundary" of which incorporates its four equilateral triangular faces. To find the boundary of this boundary, one would measure the clockwise- or counterclockwise-oriented edges around each face, thus measuring each edge of the tetrahedron twice in opposite directions. Because summing the measurements now cancels to 0 at each edge, the boundary of the boundary of the tetrahedron is zero. This property turns out to have extensive applications in physics, particularly the theory of fields, as regards the mutual "grip" of matter on space and space on matter (or less colorfully, the relationship of space and matter). In Wheeler's view, its ubiquity "inspires hope that we will someday complete the mathematization of physics and derive everything from nothing, all law from no law." Thus, it is closely related to law without law and so-called *ex nihilo* creation.

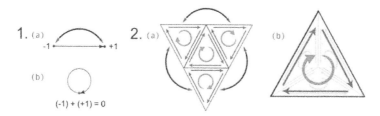

DIAGRAM IV **1a.** The boundary of a directed 1-dimensional line segment consists of its 0-dimensional endpoints, which separate the line from its complement (the space surrounding the line). The initial point represents the "debt" required to start the line and is thus given a value of -1, while the terminal point represents the "payoff" for completing the line and is given a value of +1. When the initial and terminal points of the line are identified as indicated by the curved arrow, the result is a closed line bounding a planar disk (**1b**). Because the endpoints now coincide, they sum to 0 and no longer separate the line from its complement; thus, the 0-dimensional boundary of the 1-dimensional boundary of the 2-dimensional disk is 0. **2a.** A triangular area can be decomposed into 4 smaller triangular areas. Introducing a uniform (in this case, clockwise) orientation to the areas (red arrows) imparts the same orientation to the outer perimeter (outer blue arrows), recreating the situation of 1b (notice that the blue arrows next to each interior edge point in opposite directions and therefore cancel). Again, the initial and terminal points of the perimeter coincide and cancel to 0 no matter where they lie. When adjacent perimeter segments are identified as indicated by the outer arrows, the triangle folds into a tetrahedron (**2b**). Its faces form a closed 2-dimensional boundary separating its 3-dimensional interior from its exterior, while its edges form a closed 1-dimensional boundary separating its faces from each other. But now the blue arrows cancel out at *every* edge, and the 1-dimensional boundary of the 2-dimensional boundary of the tetrahedron is 0. So for both the 2D disk and the 3D tetrahedron, the boundary of the boundary is 0. While physicists often use this rule to explain the conservation of energy-momentum – or as Wheeler (1990b) calls it, "momenergy" – it can be more generally interpreted with respect to *information* and *constraint*, or *state* and *syntax*. That is, the boundary is analogous to a constraint which separates an interior attribute satisfying the constraint from a complementary exterior attribute, thus creating an informational distinction.

No question? No answer! In a quantum experiment, the measuring device and its placement correspond to a question, and the result to its answer. The existence of the answer, consisting of information on state, is predicated on the asking of the question (or the occurrence of the measurement), and the kind of answer received depends on the kind of question asked and the manner in which it is posed. The world is thus composed of measurement events in which information is exchanged by objects, one or both of which "ask a question" and one or both of which "give an answer". Question and answer, the stimulation and observation of an event, cannot be separated on the ontological level, and they cannot be shielded from the influence of the environment. At the root of this criterion are quantum uncertainty and complementarity, the foundation-stones of quantum mechanics.

The Super-Copernican Principle Just as Copernicus displaced geocentricity with heliocentricity, showing by extension that no particular place in the universe is special and thereby repudiating "here-centeredness", the Super-Copernican Principle says that no particular point in time is special, repudiating "now-centeredness". Essentially, this means that where observer-participation functions retroactively, the participatory burden is effectively distributed throughout time. So although the "bit-size" of the universe is too great to have been completely generated by the observer-participants who have thus far existed, future generations of observer-participants, possibly representing modes of observer-participation other than that associated with human observation, have been and are now weighing in from the future. (The relevance of this principle to the Participatory Anthropic Principle is self-evident.)

"Consciousness" Wheeler emphasizes the difficulty of making a general distinction between the form of information processing characteristic of humans, and that characteristic of various complex systems and devices that may or may not be "conscious". "The line between the unconscious and the conscious begins to fade . . . ," he states. "We may someday have to enlarge the scope of what we mean by a 'who'." The term *who*, he suggests, is too specific to man, life and consciousness; its anthropic connotations are anti-Copernican, while the concepts of life and consciousness are subject to revision as science advances. "It would seem more reasonable," he suggests, "to dismiss for the present the semantic overtones of 'who' and explore and exploit the insights to be won from the phrases, 'communication' and 'communication employed to establish meaning'."

More is different The potential for complexity increases with cardinality; with large numbers of elements comes combinatorial variety and the potential for the sort of multilevel logical structure that typifies biological organisms and modern computers alike. This is a fundamental precept of complexity theory. Wheeler poses a question: "Will we someday understand time and space and all the other features that distinguish physics – and existence itself – as the . . . self-generated organs of a self-synthesized information system?"

Together, these pithy slogans, questions, precautions and clues add up to a call for a new strain of reality theory, a unified conceptual model for our thoughts and observations. How many of the models currently being held forth respond to this call? The answer, of course, is "almost none". While some of them seem to address one or two of the questions and meet one or two of the criteria, none comes close to addressing and meeting all of them. What each model has been forced to give in order to meet any small subset of criteria has cost it dearly in terms of meeting the others. Thus, we have thesis and antithesis in the form of classical physics and discrete quantum models, but because the full depth of the relationship between the two is unfathomed, no synthesis. Virtually everybody seems to acknowledge the correctness of Wheeler's insights, but the higher-order relationships required to put it all together in one big picture have proven elusive. The logical difficulty of answering all of the questions and meeting all of the criteria at once, in parallel, using integrated, logically tractable concepts, has simply been prohibitive.

Can this situation be redressed?

5 Some Additional Principles

Although insights regarding the ideal and/or perceptual basis of reality go back millennia, we may as well start with some their more recent proponents for the sake of continuity. First, Descartes posited that reality is mental in the sense of rationalism, but contradicted his own thesis by introducing *mind-body dualism*, the notion that mind and matter are irreducibly separate. The empiricist Berkeley then said that reality is perceptual in nature, a kind of intersect of mind and matter. This can be seen by mentally subtracting perception from one's conception of reality; what remains is pure subjective cognition, but without any objective grist for the perceptual mill. (Although attempts to cognitively subtract cognition from reality are far more common, they are a bit like trying to show that a sponge is not inherently wet while immersing it in water, and can never be successful on the parts of cognitive entities.) Hume then attempted to do away with cognition and causation entirely, asserting that both mind and matter inhere in perception and exist apart from neither it nor each other.

In disposing of mind, Hume made another salient "contribution" to reality theory: he attempted to dispose of causation by identifying it as a cognitive artifact, supporting his thesis with the *problem of induction*.[5] The problem of induction states that because empirical induction entails the prior assumption of that which it seeks to establish, namely the uniformity of nature, science is circular and fundamentally flawed. The problem of induction is very real; it is manifest in Heisenberg uncertainty and the cosmic horizon problem, finite limitations of scientific tools of microscopic and macroscopic observation, and is why no general theory of reality can ever be reliably constructed by the standard empirical methods of science. Unfortunately, many scientists have either dismissed this problem or quietly given up on the search for a truly general theory, in neither case serving the long-term interests of science. In fact, the problem of induction merely implies that a global theory of reality can only be established by the rational methods of mathematics, specifically including those of logic.

In response to Berkeley and Hume, Kant asserted that the unprimed cognition which remains when perceptual content is subtracted has intrinsic structure that exists *prior* to content; it comprises the *a priori* categories of perceptual or "phenomenal" reality (Russell, 1979). Unfortunately, subtracting perception according to Kantian rules yields more than unprimed cognition; it also yields noumena, absolute objects or "things-in-themselves". On one side of the result is a perceptual isomorphism between the mind and phenomenal reality; on the other yawns a chasm on the far side of which sits

---

[5] We will ignore for now the fact that if the mind is illusory, then so is all philosophy including Hume's, and if causation is illusory, then so is the form of causation represented by logical implication, including Hume's use of logical implication to define his philosophy.

an unknowable but nonetheless fundamental noumenal reality, which Kant evidently regarded as the last word in (sub-theological) reality theory.

However, Kant's chasm is so deep and wide, and so thoroughly interdicts any mind-reality isomorphism, that it precludes causal efficacy and for that matter any other comprehensible principle of correspondence. This implies that noumena are both rationally and empirically irrelevant to cognitive and perceptual reality, and thus that they can be safely eliminated from reality theory. Whatever Kant had in mind when he introduced the concept of a *noumenon*, his definition essentially amounts to "inconceivable concept" and is thus an oxymoron. Whatever he really meant, we must rely on something other than Kantian metaphysics to find it (Langan, 2001b).

Thus far, we have managed to narrow reality down to the phenomenal reality studied by science, a combination of perceptual content and rational principles of cognition. A scientist employs empirical methods to make specific observations, applies general cognitive relationships from logic and mathematics in order to explain them, and comes off treating reality as a blend of perception and cognition. But this treatment lacks anything resembling an explicit justification. When a set of observations is *explained* with a likely set of equations *interpreted* therein, the adhesion between explanandum and explanation might as well be provided by rubber cement. I.e., scientific explanations and interpretations glue observations and equations together in a very poorly understood way. It often works like a charm . . . but why? One of the main purposes of reality theory is to answer this question.

The first thing to notice about this question is that it involves the process of *attribution*, and that the rules of attribution are set forth in stages by mathematical logic. The first stage is called *sentential logic* and contains the rules for ascribing the attributes *true* or *false*, respectively denoting inclusion or non-inclusion in arbitrary cognitive-perceptual systems, to hypothetical relationships in which predicates are linked by the logical functors *not, and, or, implies,* and *if and only if.* Sentential logic defines these functors as *truth functions* assigning *truth values* to such expressions irrespective of the contents (but not the truth values) of their predicates, thus effecting a circular definition of functors on truth values and truth values on functors. The next stage of attribution, *predicate logic,* ascribes specific properties to objects using quantifiers. And the final stage, *model theory,* comprises the rules for attributing complex relations of predicates to complex relations of objects, i.e. theories to universes. In addition, the form of attribution called *definition* is explicated in a theory-centric branch of logic called *formalized theories,* and the mechanics of functional attribution is treated in recursion theory.

In sentential logic, a *tautology* is an expression of functor-related sentential variables that is always true, regardless of the truth values assigned to its sentential variables themselves. A tautology has three key properties: it is universally (syntactically) true, it is thus self-referential (true even of itself and therefore closed under recursive self-composition), and its implications remain consistent under inferential operations preserving these properties. That is, every tautology is a self-consistent circularity of universal scope, possessing validity by virtue of closure under self-composition, comprehensiveness (non-exclusion of truth), and consistency (freedom from irresolvable paradox). But tautologies are not merely consistent unto themselves; they are mutually consistent under mutual composition, making sentential logic as much a "self-consistent circularity of universal scope" as any one of its tautologies. Thus, sentential logic embodies two levels of tautology, one applying to expressions and one applying to theoretical systems thereof. Predicate logic then extends the tautology concept to cover the specific acts of attribution represented by (formerly anonymous) sentential variables, and model theory goes on to encompass more complex acts of attribution involving more complex relationships.

Reality theory is about the stage of attribution in which two predicates analogous to true and false, namely *real* and *unreal*, are ascribed to various statements about the real universe. In this sense, it is closely related to sentential logic. In particular, sentential logic has four main properties to be emulated by reality theory. The first is *absolute truth*; as the formal definition of truth, it is true by definition. The other properties are *closure, comprehensiveness* and *consistency*. I.e., logic is wholly based on, and defined strictly within the bounds of, cognition and perception; it applies to everything that can be coherently perceived or conceived; and it is by its very nature consistent, being designed in a way that precludes inconsistency. It is the basis of mathematics, being the means by which propositions are stated, proved or disproved, and it is the core of science, underwriting the integrity of rational and empirical methodology. Even so-called "nonstandard" logics, e.g. modal, fuzzy and many-valued logics, must be expressed in terms of fundamental two-valued logic to make sense. In short, two-valued logic is something without which reality could not exist. If it were eliminated, then *true* and *false*, *real* and *unreal*, and *existence* and *nonexistence* could not be distinguished, and the merest act of perception or cognition would be utterly impossible.

Thus far, it has been widely assumed that reality theory can be sought by the same means as any other scientific theory. But this is not quite true, for while science uses the epistemological equivalent of magic glue to attach its theories to its observations, reality theory must give a recipe for the glue and justify the means of application. That is, reality theory must describe reality on a level that justifies science, and thus occupies a deeper level of explanation than science itself. Does this mean that reality theory is mathematical? Yes, but since mathematics must be justified along with science, *metamathematical* would perhaps be a better description . . . and when all is said and done, this comes down to logic pure and simple. It follows that reality theory must take the form of an extended logic . . . in fact, a "limiting form" of logic in which the relationship between theory and universe, until now an inexhaustible source of destructive model-theoretic ambiguity, is at last reduced to (dual-aspect) monic form, short-circuiting the paradox of Cartesian dualism and eliminating the epistemological gap between mind and matter, theory and universe.

As complexity rises and predicates become theories, tautology and truth become harder to recognize. Because universality and specificity are at odds in practice if not in principle, they are subject to a kind of "logical decoherence" associated with relational stratification. Because predicates are not always tautological, they are subject to various kinds of ambiguity; as they become increasingly specific and complex, it becomes harder to locally monitor the heritability of consistency and locally keep track of the truth property in the course of attribution (or even after the fact). Undecidability (Gödel, 1962), LSAT intractability and NP-completeness, predicate ambiguity and the Löwenheim–Skolem theorem, observational ambiguity and the Duhem–Quine thesis[6] . . . these are some of the problems that emerge once the truth predicate "decoheres" with respect to complex attributive mappings. It is for reasons like these that the philosophy of science has fallen back on falsificationist doctrine, giving up on the tautological basis of logic, effectively demoting truth to provisional status, and discouraging full appreciation of the tautological-syntactic level of scientific inquiry even in logic and philosophy themselves.

In fact, the validity of scientific theories and of science as a whole absolutely depends on the existence of a fundamental reality-theoretic framework spanning all of science . . . a fundamental syntax from which all scientific and mathematical languages, and the extended cognitive language of perception itself, can be grammatically unfolded, cross-related and validated. Tautology, the theoretical basis of truth as embodied in sentential logic, is obviously the core of this syntax. Accordingly, reality theory must be developed through amplification of this tautological syntax by adjunction of additional syntactic components, the principles of reality theory, which leave the overall character of the syntax invariant. Specifically, in order to fashion a reality theory that has the truth property in the same sense as does logic, but permits the logical evaluation of statements about space and time and law, we must adjoin principles of extension that lend meaning to such statements while preserving the tautology property.

According to the nature of sentential logic, truth is tautologically based on the integrity of cognitive and perceptual reality. Cognition and perception comprise the primitive (self-definitive) basis of logic, and logic comprises the rules of structure and inference under which perception and cognition are stable and coherent. So when we say that truth is heritable under logical rules of inference, we really mean that *tautology* is heritable, and that the primitive cognitive-perceptual basis of sentential logic thus maintains its primary status. By converting tautologies into other tautologies, the rules of inference of sentential logic convert cognitive-perceptual invariants into other such

---

[6] For more on the Löwenheim-Skolem theorem and Duhem-Quine thesis, *see* Langan, C. M. (2002b).

invariants. To pursue this agenda in reality theory, we must identify principles that describe how the looping structure of logical tautology is manifest in various reality-theoretic settings and contexts on various levels of description and interpretation; that way, we can verify its preservation under the operations of theoretic reduction and extension. I.e., we must adjoin generalized principles of loop structure to logical syntax in such a way that more and more of reality is thereby explained and comprehensiveness is achieved.

For example, take the sentential tautology $X \lor \sim X$ (X or not-X). Applied to perception, this means that when something is seen or observed, it is not seen in conjunction with its absence; if it were, then two contradictory perceptions would coincide, resulting in a "splitting off" of perceptual realities. In effect, either the consciousness of the perceiver would split into two separate cognitive realities in a case of chain-reactive dissociation, or the perceiver himself would physically split along with physical reality. When $X \lor \sim X$ is composed with other tautologies (or itself) by substitution, the stakes are exactly the same; any violation of the compound tautology would split perceptual and cognitive reality with disastrous implications for its integrity.[7]

After its tautological nature, the first thing to note about sentential logic in the context of reality theory is that against the spirit in which it was founded – it does, after all, represent the rules of the *mental* processes[8] of cognition and perception, which would seem to endow it with a mental character from the start – it has a basic functional inadequacy: it seems to require an external logician to mentally read, understand and apply it. On the other hand, nature (or cognitive-perceptual reality) requires no external logician to apply the rules of logic. Therefore, the proposed tautology-preserving principles of reality theory should put mind back into the mix in an explicit, theoretically tractable way, effectively endowing logic with "self-processing capability". This, after all, is exactly what it possesses in its natural manifestation, reality at large, and is an essential dimension of the closure property without which truth is insupportable. That is, reality must be able to recognize itself and impart this ability to its components as a condition of their existence and interaction.

---

[7] The Many Worlds interpretation of quantum mechanics, in claiming to circumvent the problem of quantum mechanical wave function collapse, in effect claims to circumvent the problem of split consciousness as well. However, since MW is itself necessarily formulated in terms of two-valued logic, the problem regresses to that of how the "hyperuniverse" associated with MW itself "collapsed" out of the sea of all potential "meta-realities". On this score, MW has little insight to offer on its own behalf. MW thus lacks justificative self-containment and is therefore no basis for a fundamental theory of reality. In any case, since the theory we are describing in this paper is designed to address reality in its most basic form, and thus to address all conceivable realities as its possible instantiations, it supersedes any explanation afforded by MW alone.

[8] Several millennia ago, Aristotle proposed (categorical) logic as the formal rules of correct reasoning. Now as then, "reasoning" is inferential, mental and subjective in nature. After standing largely changeless until the nineteenth century, the field of logic began to undergo additional progress. But although this progress has been considerable, it has left the inferential, mental and subjective nature of logic essentially intact.

Having explained the main technical issues in reality theory, we may now cut to the chase: the way to build a theory of reality is to identify the properties that it must unconditionally possess in order to exist, and then bring the theory into existence by defining it to possess these properties without introducing merely contingent properties that, if taken as general, could impair its descriptive relationship with the real universe (those can come later and will naturally be subject to empirical confirmation). In other words, the means by which the theory is constructed must be rational and tautological, while those by which it is subsequently refined may be empirical. Since we want our theory to be inclusive enough, exclusive enough and consistent enough to do the job of describing reality, these properties will certainly include *comprehensiveness* (less thorough but also less undecidable than completeness), *closure*, and *consistency*. To these properties, the "3 C's", we shall assign three principles that are basically tautological in form; that way, adjoining them to logic-based reality theory will preserve the tautology property of logic, rationally precluding uncertainty by the same means as logic itself. A theory of reality constructed in this way is called a *supertautology*.

Because our three principles correspond to the 3 C's, and because they all begin with the letter M, we might as well call them the "3 M's": M=R, MAP and MU, respectively standing for the *Mind Equals Reality Principle*, the *Metaphysical Autology Principle*, and the *Multiplex Unity Principle*. The M=R principle, a tautological theoretical property that dissolves the distinction between *theory* and *universe* and thus identifies the real universe as a "self-reifying theory", makes the syntax of this theory comprehensive by ensuring that nothing which can be cognitively or perceptually recognized as a part of reality is excluded for want of syntax. MAP tautologically renders this syntax closed or self-contained in the definitive, descriptive and interpretational senses, and in conjunction with M=R, renders the universe perfectly self-contained in the bargain. And MU tautologically renders this syntax, and the theory-universe complex it describes, coherent enough to ensure its own consistency (thus, the "C" corresponding to MU actually splits into two C's, *consistency* and *coherence*, and we have four altogether). To each of these principles we may add any worthwhile corollaries that present themselves.[9]

Since it is the lot of every reality theorist to use properties of reality to explain reality, and these properties are recursively defined, we will sometimes implicitly or explicitly refer to various properties in the descriptions of other properties. This precludes a neat series of cumulative definitions, which is possible in any case only by taking for granted the content and wherewithal of theorization (unfortunately, one can take nothing for granted in reality theory). As we will see below, the recursive nature of the CTMU is unavoidable. Secondly, the CTMU is developed "backwards" with respect to the usual

---

[9] Note that while this seems to imply that the 3 M's are "axioms" and therefore independent, the premise of axiomatic independence is itself a rather flimsy concept. These principles are actually rather strongly related in the sense that they can to some extent be inferred from each other in a reality-theoretic context.

deductive theories of science and mathematics, by first peeling away constraints and only then using the results to deduce facts about content. Most theories begin with axioms, hypotheses and rules of inference, extract implications, logically or empirically test these implications, and then add or revise axioms, theorems or hypotheses. The CTMU does the opposite, stripping away assumptions and "rebuilding reality" while adding no assumptions back.

The following principles are presented in three stages. The first stage includes the *Reality Principle*, the *Principle of Linguistic Reducibility* and the *Principle of Syndiffeonesis*, which may be considered preliminary to MAP, M=R and MU respectively (the order of presentation may differ slightly from that just given). The second stage consists of MAP, M=R and MU themselves, while the third stage consists of several auxiliary principles that can be viewed as their consequences.

5.1 The Reality Principle

Reality, i.e. the real universe, contains all and only that which is real. The reality concept is analytically self-contained; if there were something *outside* reality that were *real* enough to affect or influence reality, it would be *inside* reality, and this contradiction invalidates any supposition of an external reality (up to observational or theoretical relevance).[10]

While this characterization of reality incorporates a circular definition of relevance, the circularity is essential to the reality concept and does not preclude a perceptual (observational, scientific) basis. Indeed, we can refine the definition of reality as follows: "Reality is the perceptual aggregate including (1) all scientific observations that ever were and ever will be, and (2) the entire abstract and/or cognitive explanatory infrastructure of perception" (where the *abstract* is a syntactic generalization of the *concrete* standing for ideas, concepts or cognitive structures distributing over physical instances which conform to them as content conforms to syntax).

It should be noted that any definition amounts to a microscopic theory of the thing defined. The Reality Principle, which can be viewed as a general definition of reality, is a case in point; it can be viewed as the seed of a reality theory that we have now begun to build. In defining reality as self-contained, this "microtheory" endows itself with a simple kind of closure; it calls on nothing outside the definiendum in the course of defining it, and effectively forbids any future theoretical extension of this definition from doing so either (this becomes explicit in a related principle, the *MAP*).

---

[10] In physics, the phrase "Reality Principle" has sometimes been associated with the idea that objective reality exists independently of human observation, at least to the extent that it does not suddenly disappear when not being directly watched. As used in this paper, the phrase "Reality Principle" is to be interpreted as described in this section unless otherwise indicated.

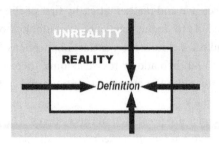

DIAGRAM V Unreal "Definition of Reality".

But now back to the queue. Thus far, we have learned that reality is self-contained; it is everywhere the same as itself. What about all of its internal distinctions?

5.2 Syndiffeonesis

Reality is a relation, and every relation is a *syndiffeonic* relation exhibiting *syndiffeonesis* or "difference-in-sameness". Therefore, reality is a syndiffeonic relation. Syndiffeonesis implies that any assertion to the effect that two things are different implies that they are reductively the same; if their difference is real, then they both reduce to a common reality and are to that extent similar. Syndiffeonesis, the most general of all reductive principles, forms the basis of a new view of the relational structure of reality.

The concept of syndiffeonesis can be captured by asserting that the expression and/or existence of any difference relation entails a common medium and *syntax*, i.e. the rules of state and transformation characterizing the medium. It is from these rules that the relation derives its spatial and temporal characteristics as expressed within the medium. Thus, a syndiffeonic relation consists of a difference relation embedded in a relational medium whose distributed rules of structure and evolution support its existence.

Every syndiffeonic relation has *synetic* and *diffeonic* phases respectively exhibiting *synesis* and *diffeonesis* (sameness and difference, or distributivity and parametric locality), and displays two forms of containment, *topological* and *descriptive*. The medium is associated with the synetic phase, while the difference relation is associated with the diffeonic phase (because the rules of state and transformation of the medium are distributed over it, the medium is homogeneous, intrinsically possessing only relative extension by virtue of the difference relationships it contains). Because diffeonic relands are related to their common expressive medium and its distributive syntax in a way that combines aspects of union and intersection, the operation producing the medium from the relands is called *unisection* (∪∩). The synetic medium represents diffeonic *potential* of which the difference relationship is an *actualization*.

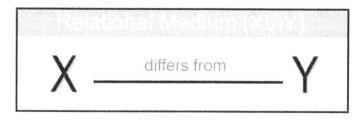

DIAGRAM VI This generic **syndiffeonic diagram** illustrates a simple fact: any difference relation requires a supporting medium with extension in the differential parameter. As illustrated, the medium distributes over both the linear relation "X differs from Y" and its *relands* (related entities) X and Y, bestowing on them a common "relatedness" property equating to "inclusion in the relational medium X∪Y", where X∪Y is the unisect or "syntactic product" of X and Y. This common attribute invalidates any assertion to the effect that the difference between the relands is "absolute" or "irreducible"; the mere fact that the difference can be linguistically or geometrically expressed implies that it is only partial and that both relands are manifestations of one and the same ontological medium. Where X and Y represent arbitrary parts or aspects of the difference relation called *reality*, this diagram graphically demonstrates that reality ultimately consists of a unitary ontological medium. Accordingly, reality theory must be a monic theory reducing reality to this medium (this idea is further developed in the *Principle of Infocognitive Monism*).

Note that any syntactic (as opposed to informational) inhomogeneity in the common medium is itself a difference relationship and thus invites a recreation of the diagram. Similarly, any inhomogeneity in the common medium illustrated by the recreated diagram would invite yet another recreation of the diagram, and so on. Any such syndiffeonic regress must terminate, for if it did not, there would be no stable syntax and therefore no "relation" stable enough to be perceived or conceived. The informational stability of perceptual reality shows that reality has a stable syntax.

The above diagram might be compactly expressed as follows: $\mathrm{syn}(X \cap Y) : \mathrm{diff}(X, Y)$. For example, $\mathrm{syn}(\mathrm{nom}_A X \cap \mathrm{nom}_B X) : \mathrm{diff}(\mathrm{nom}_A X, \mathrm{nom}_B X)$ means that where $\mathrm{nom}_A X$, $\mathrm{nom}_B X$ are sets of laws obeyed by the system X at different times, locations or frames of reference A and B within the system X, there exists a more basic set of laws $(\mathrm{nom}_A X \cap \mathrm{nom}_B X)$ in terms of which this difference may be expressed. This shows that on some level, general covariance must hold. This is not merely true "up to isomorphism with X"; even if more than one valid set of laws can be distinguished, any one of which might be active at any given location $(A, B, \ldots)$ within X $[X_A \vDash \mathrm{nom}_1, X_B \vDash \mathrm{nom}_2, \ldots,$ where numerical indices denote nomological distinctness], any distinguishable difference between these sets also requires a common syntax. Informational coherence is thus a *sine qua non* of recognizable existence; any system in which it were to fail would simply decohere for lack of anything to hold it together.

In other words, (1) where informational distinctions regarding a system X are regarded as instantiations of law, they can also be regarded as expressions conforming to syntax; and (2) the expression of differences requires a unified expressive syntax (or set of "laws"), and this syntax must distribute over the entire set of differential expressions (or "instantiations of law"). E.g., where X is a "perceptual intersect" consisting of generally recognizable objects, attributes and events, the laws of perception must ultimately be constant and distributed. Where a putative nomological difference exists for some pair of loci (A, B), reductive syntactic covariance applies due to the need for an expressive medium, and where no such difference exists for *any* pair of loci (A, B), syntactic covariance applies *a fortiori* with no need for reduction.

Syndiffeonic relations can be regarded as elements of more complex *infocognitive lattices* with spatial and temporal (ordinal, stratificative) dimensions. Interpreted according to CTMU duality principles, infocognitive lattices comprise logical relationships of *state* and *syntax*. Regressing up one of these lattices by unisection ultimately leads to a syntactic medium of perfect generality and homogeneity . . . a universal, reflexive "syntactic operator".

In effect, syndiffeonesis is a metalogical tautology amounting to *self-resolving paradox*. The paradox resides in the coincidence of sameness and difference, while a type-theoretic resolution inheres in the logical and mathematical distinction between them, i.e. the stratificative dimension of an infocognitive lattice.[11] Thus, reducing reality to syndiffeonesis amounts to "paradoxiforming" it. This has an advantage: a theory and/or reality built of self-resolving paradox is immunized to paradox.

So far, we know that reality is a self-contained syndiffeonic relation. We also have access to an instructive sort of diagram that we can use to illustrate some of the principles which follow. So let us see if we can learn more about the *kind* of self-contained syndiffeonic relation that reality is.

5.3 The Principle of Linguistic Reducibility

Reality is a self-contained form of language. This is true for at least two reasons. First, although it is in some respects material and concrete, reality conforms to the algebraic definition of a language. That is, it incorporates:

(1) representations of (object-like) individuals, (space-like) relations and attributes, and (time-like) functions and operations;

(2) a set of "expressions" or perceptual states;

(3) a syntax consisting of (a) logical and geometric rules of structure, and (b) an inductive-deductive generative grammar identifiable with the laws of state transition.

Second, because perception and cognition are languages, and reality is cognitive and perceptual in nature, reality is a language as well.

---

[11] The type-theoretic resolution of this paradox is incomplete; full resolution requires MU, a kind of "meta-syndiffeonesis" endowing the infocognitive lattice of spacetime with a higher level of closure.

While there have been many reductionist programs in science and philosophy, the promised reduction is always to the same thing: a theoretical language. Because this is necessarily true, language is fundamental. The fact that most such theories, e.g. theories of physics, point to the fundamental status of something "objective" and "independent of language", e.g. matter and/or energy, is quite irrelevant, for the very act of pointing invokes an isomorphism between theory and objective reality . . . an isomorphism that is subject to the Reality Principle, and which could not exist unless reality shared the linguistic structure of the theory itself.

Perhaps the meaning of this principle can be most concisely expressed through a generalization of the aphorism "whereof one cannot speak, one must be silent": *whereof that which cannot be linguistically described, one cannot perceive or conceive.* So for the observational and theoretical purposes of science and reality theory, that which is nonisomorphic to language is beyond consideration as a component of reality.

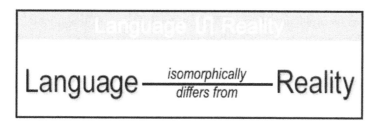

DIAGRAM VII In this syndiffeonic diagram, the assertion "Language differs from reality" is laid out along an extended line segment representing the supposed difference between the relands. Just as in the generic diagram above, both relands possess the attribute "inclusion in the relational syntactic medium (Language ∩ Reality)". Because they are both manifestations of the same underlying medium, their difference cannot be absolute; on a fundamental level, reality and language share common aspects. This is consistent with the nature of the "difference" relationship, which is actually supposed to represent a semantic and model-theoretic isomorphism.

As we have already seen, the Reality Principle says that reality contains all and only that which is real. As defined by this statement, the predicate *reality* is primarily a linguistic construct conforming to syntactic structure, where *syntax* consists of the rules by which predicates are constructed and interpreted. In this sense, *reality* amounts to a kind of *theory* whose axioms and rules of inference are implicitly provided by the logical component of the conceptual syntax in which it is expressed. The Principle of Linguistic Reducibility merely clarifies the issue of whether *reality* is a linguistic predicate or the objective content of such a predicate by asserting that it is both. Thus, where the reality *predicate* is analytically (or syntactically) self-contained, *reality* is self-contained. This can be expressed as follows: on the level of cognitive-perceptual syntax, *reality* equals *reality theory*. Where theory and universe converge, Occam's razor and physical principles of economy become tautologies.

Because perception is a sensory intersect of mind and reality, perception is impossible without cognition, and to this extent the cognitive predicate *reality* equates to its perceptual content. On the level of cognitive and perceptual syntax, language is necessarily isomorphic to that which it describes; in a perceptual reality like that which exists around us, it is tautologically true that the basic language of cognition and perception is syntactically isomorphic to reality (though illusion and falsehood become possible on the semantic level). It follows that we can speak of reality in terms of *generalized cognition and perception*, where this phrase denotes conformance to cognition and perception on the syntactic level. In particular, generalized cognition is that process through which reality everywhere "recognizes" itself.

The Principle of Linguistic Reducibility provides a mandate to add an advanced form of language theory to the mathematical arsenal of reality theory. The reality-theoretic benefits of this addition are incalculable. In conventional physical theory, the fundamental entities are point particles, waves and more recently, strings; each class of object has its problems and paradoxes. In the CTMU, the fundamental objects are *syntactic operators* (units of self-transducing information or *infocognition*) that are not only capable of emulating all of these objects and more, but of containing the syntactic structures to which they must inevitably conform and resolving their characteristic paradoxes in the bargain. Because meaning equates to semantic connectivity and is thus linguistic in every sense of the term, the shift to a linguistic perspective is indispensable to teleology or any other form of meaning.

Now we know that reality is a *linguistic* self-contained syndiffeonic relation, although we still seem to be knowing it from an external vantage in a rather inspecific way. Where should we go next in search of clues? At this point, we could really use a MAP.

5.4 Syntactic Closure: The Metaphysical Autology Principle (MAP)

All relations, mappings and functions relevant to reality in a generalized effective sense, whether descriptive, definitive, compositional, attributive, nomological or interpretative, are generated, defined and parameterized within reality itself. In other words, reality comprises a "closed descriptive manifold" from which no essential predicate is omitted, and which thus contains no critical gap that leaves any essential aspect of structure unexplained. Any such gap would imply non-closure.

MAP, a theoretical refinement of the self-containment criterion set forth by the Reality Principle, extends the closure property of the definition of reality to the set of all real predicates. MAP effects closure on the definitive, descriptive, explanatory and interpretative levels of reality theory by making it take the form of a closed network of coupled definitions, descriptions, explanations and interpretations that refer to nothing external to reality itself. Another way to state this is that MAP, like the Reality Principle,

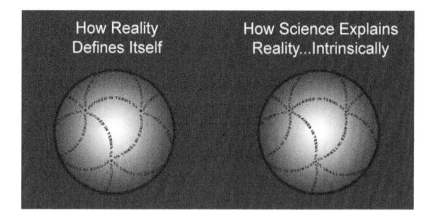

DIAGRAM VIII

requires that everything to which any reality-theoretic definition, description, explanation or interpretation refers be located within reality. This has the effect of making reality responsible for its own structure and evolution in the abstract and concrete senses. MAP requires a closed-form explanation on the grounds that distinguishability is impossible without it. Again this comes down to the issue of syntactic stability.[12] To state it in as simple a way as possible, reality must ultimately possess a stable 2-valued object-level distinction between that which it *is* and that which it *is not*, maintaining the necessary informational boundaries between objects, attributes and events. The existence of closed informational boundaries within a system is ultimately possible only by virtue of systemic closure under dualistic (*explanans-explanandum*) composition, which is just how it is effected in sentential logic.

As an example of the tautological nature of MAP, consider a hypothetical external scale of distance or duration in terms of which the absolute size or duration of the universe or its contents can be defined. Due to the analytic self-containment of reality, the functions and definitions comprising its self-descriptive manifold refer only to each other; anything not implicated in its syntactic network is irrelevant to structure and internally unrecognizable, while anything which is relevant is already an implicit ingredient of the network and need not be imported from outside. This implies that if the proposed scale is relevant, then it is not really external to reality; in fact, reality already contains it as an implication of its intrinsic structure.

---

[12] A syndiffeonic regress ultimately leads to a stable closed syntax in which all terms are mutually defined; mutual definition is what stabilizes and lends internal determinacy (internal identifiability of events) to the system through syntactic symmetry. I.e., relational closure orthogonal to the (temporal) dimension of regress amounts to the distribution of a systemic identity, and unless this identity is fully defined, the identities of system components cannot be defined or recognized by or with respect to each other. Thus, the dynamic identity is a self-identification function with definitive, descriptive and interpretative dimensions.

In other words, because reality is defined on the mutual relevance of its essential parts and aspects, *external* and *irrelevant* are synonymous; if something is external to reality, then it is not included in the syntax of reality and is thus internally unrecognizable. It follows that with respect to that level of reality defined on relevance and recognition, there is no such thing as a "real but external" scale, and thus that the universe is externally undefined with respect to all measures including overall size and duration. If an absolute scale were ever to be internally recognizable as an ontological necessity, then this would simply imply the existence of a deeper level of reality to which the scale *is* intrinsic and by which it is itself intrinsically explained as a relative function of other ingredients. Thus, if the need for an *absolute* scale were ever to become recognizable within reality – that is, recognizable to reality itself – it would by definition be relative in the sense that it could be defined and explained in terms of other ingredients of reality. In this sense, MAP is a "general principle of relativity".[13]

The "no gaps" criterion of MAP permits no critical explanatory holes omitting any essential aspect of structure. What this means can best be illustrated by means of a recurrent fallacy: "The existence of the universe is given and therefore in no need of explanation." The phrase *is given* is incomplete; it has hidden "loose ends" corresponding to *that by which* existence is given, the *means by which* it is given, and the *reason for which* it is given. If the source, means and reason are actually real, then they are inside reality, and the explanatory gap exists only in the mind of the claimant rather than in the self-explanatory network of reality itself.

On the other hand, omitting this phrase (*is given*) results in something like "the existence of the universe is inexplicable". However, this amounts to the assertion that the universe has no identifiable basis or medium of existence, *not even itself* . . . i.e., that no explanatory function can be defined on the explanandum, and that the universe is somehow prohibited from serving as its own source, means, or reason. But this amounts to saying that the universe could only exist "by magic", popping out of the *apeiron* with a spontaneity exceeding that by which a genuine magician might pull a magic rabbit out of a hat. For whereas magic rabbits can at least be said to originate by magic associated with magicians who pull them out of top hats into the bright light of reality, or to magically bootstrap themselves out of their own hats into their own realities, the universe would be denied any ontological basis or medium whatsoever . . . even a bootstrap.

---

[13] It is tempting to note that "relativity" means roughly the same thing in the General Theory of Relativity as it does here. That is, using a distributed-syntactic "tangent space", the structure of spacetime is tensorially defined in terms of the masses and relative positions of its own material contents, resulting in an intrinsic MAP-like definition of spacetime. Unfortunately, the basic formalism of GR, differential geometry, is not self-contained with respect to time; as currently formulated, it tacitly relies on an embedding (conspansive) medium to provide it with temporal potential.

Because questions like "why and how does reality exist (within the domain of existential potential supporting the possibility of existence)?" and "why does this reality exist instead of some other reality?"[14] address the ontological or teleological levels of the structure of reality, and because these levels of structure are logically meaningful, they must have answers . . . even if those answers are determined, as some of them are, by the closure criterion itself.

Now we know that the closed, single-predicate definition of the Reality Principle is actually a closed descriptive manifold of linked definitions in principle containing the means of its own composition, attribution, recognition, processing and interpretation. But this is still somewhat automatonic. What about *mind*? Since it is through our minds that we understand anything at all, understanding remains incomplete until we understand more about the relationship between mind and reality. So, having equipped ourselves with a MAP, we now attend to the correspondence between the MAP and the terrain.

5.5 Syntactic Comprehensivity-Reflexivity: The Mind Equals Reality Principle (M=R)

The M=R or *Mind Equals Reality* Principle asserts that mind and reality are ultimately inseparable to the extent that they share common rules of structure and processing. The existence of a difference relation between mind and reality syndiffeonically presupposes a relational medium having the characteristics of both, and this medium has logical priority over the difference relation itself.

The M=R principle is merely a logical version of what empiricist philosophers long ago pointed out: we experience reality in the form of perceptions and sense data from which the existence and independence of mind and objective external reality are induced. Since any proof to the contrary would necessarily be cognitive, as are all "proofs", and since the content of cognition is cognitive by embedment, no such proof can exist; such a proof would undermine its own medium and thereby cancel itself. On the other hand, the Reality Principle says that reality is self-contained with respect to recognition and control, and to the extent that recognition and control are "mental" (in the sense of being effected according to cognitive and perceptual syntax), so is reality. The M=R Principle entails comprehensivity by defining all of our perceptions, along with their syntax-

---

[14] What such a question really asks is "why does the habitation and observation relationship holding between the observer/questioner and the universe exist?" The Weak Anthropic Principle goes halfway toward an answer by applying a probabilistic selection function: "the relationship has been logically selected by the fact that only certain kinds of universe can accommodate acts of observation and an observer like the questioner." This is right as far as it goes, but omits the generative, pre-selective phase of the explanation . . . the part that accounts for the selection function and the domain to which it is applied. In this respect, the WAP is a bit like natural selection; it weeds the garden well enough, but is helpless to grow a single flower.

DIAGRAM IX M=R (Mind = Reality) Principle. In the above syndiffeonic diagram, mind is juxtaposed with reality in a space bounded by a box. The line separating mind and reality represents the supposed difference between them, while the interior of the box represents their comparability or "relatedness" (or more technically, their uniform differentiating syntax or unisect, denoted by means of the ∪ functor). The extensionality of the line is just that of the box; without the box, there would be no extensional medium to contain the line, and no way to express the associated difference relation. Because the separation cannot exist without a common medium incorporating a differentiative syntax that distributes over both relands of the difference relation, the "absolute separation" of mind and reality has no model . . . and without a model, the premise of Cartesian mind-matter dualism fails. This indicates that reality and mind, information and information processor, must ultimately be regarded as one. Any Cartesian-style distinction between them must be strictly qualified.

level cognitive-syntactic infrastructure, as parts of reality regardless of decidability.[15] When it comes to M=R, it is hard to resist a little play on words: M=R says that at the syntactic level of cognition and perception, "the MAP is the terrain." Note that M=R goes beyond the mere Kantian isomorphism between phenomenal reality and the categories of thought and perception; it says that syntax and its content are recursively related, and in conjunction with the Reality Principle, that any supposed "content" not related to the rules of structure and evolution of reality is irrelevant. (Although this is a trivial observation insofar as "unrelated" and "irrelevant" are synonymous, it seems to have been largely ignored by many who should have known better.)

To put it another way: if the "noumenal" (perceptually independent) part of reality were truly unrelated to the phenomenal (cognition-isomorphic) part, then these two "halves" of reality would neither be coincident nor share a joint medium relating them. In that case, they would simply fall apart, and any integrated "reality" supposedly containing both of them would fail for lack of an integrated model. Where M (mind) is identified with cognition and R (reality) with physically-embodied information, M=R says that reality everywhere consists of a common substance, infocognition, having the dual nature of mind and (informational) reality.

---

[15] Note that the M=R Principle does not assert (e.g.) that the fruits of human imagination are "real" except as neural firing patterns with no necessary relevance to anything outside the brain, or that we can immediately make things "real" just by thinking of them. The M=R principle merely says that where mind is the engine of cognition and perception, and these processes are jointly regarded as a "language" obeying rules of syntax, this syntax – the rules of cognition and perception – necessarily distributes over percipient and percept.

The M=R property takes up where the Principle of Linguistic Reducibility leaves off in eliminating the distinction between theory and universe. By its light, the theoretical description of reality by human beings contained in reality amounts to reality describing itself. (Bearing in mind that a theory is a mental construct, this can be illustrated by simply replacing Mind and Reality in the above diagram by Theory and Universe, and *Mind ∩ Reality* by *Theory ∩ Universe*.) It thus makes the theory reflexive and thus inclusive enough by definition to describe the entire universe, including that which is rational, abstract and subjective, and that which is empirical, concrete and objective. The dissolution of this distinction can be viewed as a reduction.

So now we know that reality is more than just a linguistic self-contained syndiffeonic relation comprising a closed descriptive manifold of linked definitions containing the means of its own configuration, composition, attribution, recognition, processing and interpretation. It is also a self-processing theory identical to its universe.

5.6 Syntactic Coherence and Consistency: The Multiplex Unity Principle (MU)

The universe topologically contains that which descriptively contains the universe. MU, the minimum and most general informational configuration of reality, defines the relationship holding between unity and multiplicity, the universe and its variegated contents. Through its structure, the universe and its contents are mutually inclusive, providing each other with a medium.

In other words, we can equivalently characterize the contents of the universe as being topologically "inside" it (topological inclusion), or characterize the universe as being descriptively "inside" its contents, occupying their internal syntaxes as acquired state (descriptive inclusion). The universe generically includes its contents by serving as their syntactic unisect, while the contents contain the universe in a more specific sense involving specific event histories that become "entangled" by interaction. From the first viewpoint, the syntactic coherence of the overall medium enforces mutual consistency of contents, while from the second viewpoint, the coherent syntaxes of its contents contain and consistently recognize and transform the medium. Thus, the universe enforces its own consistency through dual self-containment.

MU expresses syndiffeonic symmetry of syntax and content on the spatiotemporal level of reality. Just as syndiffeonesis can be regarded as a paradox identifying difference with sameness, MU can be regarded as an ultimate form of paradox identifying spatiotemporal multiplicity and unity (the MU diagram is an explosion of the syndiffeonic relation diagram in which the stratification dimension is split into descriptive and topological strands or "temporal dimensions"). MU structure resolves the MU paradox *in situ* by dual stratification, providing closure as the open-ended informational stratification of type theory cannot. Because MU can thus be regarded as the resolution of the paradox

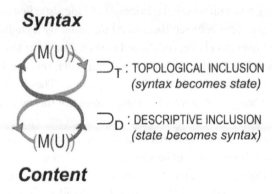

Syntax

⊃$_T$: TOPOLOGICAL INCLUSION
(syntax becomes state)

⊃$_D$: DESCRIPTIVE INCLUSION
(state becomes syntax)

Content

DIAGRAM X In the syndiffeonic **DIAGRAM VI**, we can plainly see the containment of objects by the medium, but we cannot see the containment of the medium by the objects. Bearing in mind that the terms syntax and content are to some extent relative designations, the upper node in **DIAGRAM X** corresponds to the global medium (global syntactic unisect or "metasyntax" of reality), while the lower node corresponds to the objects therein (syntactic operators contained in the medium); each is a multiplex unity. Coherence flows from global syntax into local content by way of global topological containment, thereby enforcing unity across diverse locales, and back to global syntax in multiple entangled streams generated by cross-transduction of content. Syntax becomes state, and state becomes syntax (where "syntax" is understood to encompass an "ectosyntactic" distribution of syntactic operators). The universe thus remains coherent and consistent in the course of evolution.

it describes, its meaning, like that of syndiffeonesis, can be expressed as follows: *reality is a self-resolving paradox.*

MU, by the way, need not be regarded as the ultimate guarantor of consistency; that honor can safely go to the stability of perceptual reality itself. Quite simply, the syntactic stability of reality overrides any and all objections regarding the limitations of formal systems. MU merely describes how reality, considered as a reflexive SCSPL theory, achieves intrinsic stability in the course of evolving. Thus, it is not functioning as an algorithm guaranteed to terminate on consistency but not on inconsistency, and is therefore not in conflict with undecidability. The stability of reality affirms its consistency regardless of whether or not any lesser theory happens to be consistent.

MU serves as a unifying concept for a complex of ideas having to do with coherence and consistency in the reality-theoretic context, including hology and several CTMU duality principles.

5.7 The Principle of Hology (Self-composition)

Hology, a logical analogue of holography characterizing the most general relationship between reality and its contents, is a form of self-similarity whereby the overall structure of the universe is everywhere distributed within it as accepting and transductive syntax, resulting in a homogeneous syntactic medium. That is, because reality requires a *syntax* consisting of general laws of structure and evolution, and there is nothing but reality itself to serve this purpose, reality comprises its own self-distributed syntax under MU (which characterizes the overall relationship between syntax and content).

The hology property itself is distributed over reality. That is, the informational boundary of a coherent object (syntactic operator) is hologically multiplexed with respect to state (attribute and value) in order to define the descriptive interior of the operator as it participates in global self-processing without input. This multiplexing of possibilities is just the replication of the structure of the boundary over the interior of the boundary as a function of time. Again, the operator ultimately has nothing else in terms of which to express its spatiotemporal capacity.

Hology is implied by MAP because reality is closed under composition and attribution; it is implied by M=R because reality is composed of syntactic operators with generalized mental or cognitive functionality; and it is implied by syndiffeonesis and MU because it is an expression of the relationship between the global spatiotemporal medium and its contents.

5.8 Duality Principles

Duality is a ubiquitous concept in mathematics, appearing in fields from logic and the theory of categories to geometry and analysis. The duality relation is symmetric; if dualizing proposition A yields proposition B, then dualizing B yields A. In projective geometry, for example, the dualization operation consists of switching the terms "point" and "line" in propositions containing them, as in "Two non-coincident points determine a line" $\leftarrow$ dualize $\rightarrow$ "Two non-parallel lines determine a point." Re-stating this as "lines are functions of points" $\leftarrow$ dualize $\rightarrow$ "points are functions of lines" reveals a duality relationship between functions and arguments. Thus, in vector algebra, the *dual space* V* of a vector space V is the space of all linear functionals on V (i.e. all linear maps from V to R), while V** is the space of all linear maps from V* to R.

An even more striking form of duality is encountered in graph theory, where the *dual graph* of a planar graph transforms faces to vertices and vertices to faces without disrupting its overall pattern of adjacencies. The boundary of each face is replaced by transverse edges converging on its dual vertex (and vice versa), and the adjacency relation is redefined accordingly. Where edges are given a temporal interpretation, interesting transformations can occur; e.g., circulations along facial boundaries become "vertex spins", and motion along an edge can be characterized as an operation between the dual faces of its endpoints.

Duality principles thus come in two common varieties, one transposing spatial relations and objects, and one transposing objects or spatial relations with mappings, functions, operations or processes. The first is called *space-object* (or S-O, or $S \leftrightarrow O$) duality; the second, *time-space* (or T-S/O, or $T \leftrightarrow S/O$ duality. In either case, the central feature is a transposition of *element* and a (spatial or temporal) *relation* of elements. Together, these dualities add up to the concept of *triality*, which represents the universal possibility of consistently permuting the attributes *time, space* and *object* with respect to various structures. From this, we may extract a third kind of duality: ST-O duality. In this kind of duality, associated with something called *conspansive duality*, objects can be "dualized" to spatiotemporal transducers, and the physical universe internally "simulated" by its material contents.

M=R, MU and hology are all at least partially based on duality.

5.8.1 The Principle of Attributive / Topological-Descriptive / State-Syntax Duality

Where points belong to sets and lines are relations between points, a form of duality also holds between sets and relations or attributes, and thus between set theory and logic. Where sets *contain* their elements and attributes distributively *describe* their arguments, this implies a dual relationship between topological containment and descriptive attribution as modeled through Venn diagrams. Essentially, any containment relationship can be interpreted in two ways: in terms of position with respect to bounding lines or surfaces or hypersurfaces, as in point set topology and its geometric refinements ($\supset_T$) or in terms of descriptive distribution relationships, as in the Venn-diagrammatic grammar of logical substitution ($\supset_D$) (Langan, 1999).

Attributive or TD duality is reflected in the fact that sets and logic are described by the same algebraic structure, Boolean algebra, which expresses their dual relationship in the relationship between its two operations. Expressed in set-theoretic terms, these operations are union and intersection ($\cup, \cap$); in logical terms, they are OR and AND ($\vee, \wedge$). ($\cup, \cap$) and ($\vee, \wedge$) are related as follows: the *union* ($A \cup B$) of two sets A and B consists of all and only the elements that belong to either A *or* B or both ($\forall x \in A \cup B : x \in A \vee x \in B$), while the *intersect* ($A \cap B$) of A and B consists of all and only the elements that belong to both A *and* B ($\forall x \in A \cap B : x \in A \wedge x \in B$). This kind of duality is well known; it relates to the fact that every attributive statement defining a relation of predicates can be rephrased as a statement about sets (and vice versa).

But the relationship of set theory and logic is even more interesting than this, for each has a particular representational affinity for just one of these operations. That is, set theory tends to focus on *objects* (sets and elements), while logic tends to focus on *attributes*, or informational "boundary constraints" that objects must satisfy. Thus, set theory ultimately defines sets in terms of the objects they contain, while logic tends to define them "from the outside in" on the intersecting boundary constraints to which they conform. The difference hinges on the univalent *not* functor ($\sim$), on which complementation and intersection, but not union, are directly or indirectly defined.

For example, while it is easy enough to identify an individual element or set by constructively naming or "enumerating" it, e.g. "X", identifying its complement often requires that its name be used as the basis of a restrictive constraint that can be applied across an entire finite or infinite context in one attributive operation, e.g. "not-X". The duality relationship holding between names and constraints is nicely captured by *De Morgan's Laws*, $\sim A \cap \sim B = \sim(A \cup B)$ and $\sim A \cup \sim B = \sim(A \cap B)$, which express it by permuting the objective and attributive operations $\cup$ and $\cap$.

Because states express topologically while the syntactic structures of their underlying operators express descriptively, attributive duality is sometimes called *state-syntax duality*. As information requires syntactic organization, it amounts to a valuation of cognitive / perceptual syntax; conversely, recognition consists of a subtractive restriction of informational potential through an additive acquisition of information. TD duality thus relates information to the informational potential bounded by syntax, and perception (cognitive state acquisition) to cognition.

In a Venn diagram, the contents of circles reflect the structure of their boundaries; the boundaries are the primary descriptors. The interior of a circle is simply an "interiorization" or self-distribution of its syntactic "boundary constraint". Thus, nested circles corresponding to identical objects display a descriptive form of containment corresponding to syntactic layering, with underlying levels corresponding to *syntactic coverings*.

This leads to a related form of duality, *constructive-filtrative* duality.

5.8.2 Constructive-Filtrative Duality

Any set that can be constructed by adding elements to the space between two brackets can be defined by restriction on the set of all possible sets. Restriction involves the Venn-like superposition of constraints that are subtractive in nature; thus, it is like a subtractive color process involving the stacking of filters. Elements, on the other hand, are additive, and the process of constructing sets is thus additive; it is like an additive color process involving the illumination of the color elements of pixels in a color monitor. CF duality simply asserts the general equivalence of these two kinds of process with respect to logico-geometric reality.

CF duality captures the temporal ramifications of TD duality, relating geometric operations on point sets to logical operations on predicates. Essentially, CF duality says that any geometric state or continuous transformation is equivalent to an operation involving the mutual "filtration" of intersecting hological state-potentials. States and objects, instead of being constructed from the object level upward, can be regarded as filtrative refinements of general, internally unspecified higher-order relations.

CF duality is necessary to show how a universe can be "zero-sum"; without it, there is no way to refine the objective requisites of constructive processes "from nothingness". In CTMU cosmogony, "nothingness" is informationally defined as zero constraint or pure freedom (*unbound telesis* or *UBT*), and the apparent construction of the universe is explained as a self-restriction of this potential. In a realm of unbound ontological potential, defining a constraint is not as simple as merely writing it down; because constraints act restrictively on content, constraint and content must be defined simultaneously in a unified syntax-state relationship.

5.8.3 Conspansive Duality

This principle was to some extent adumbrated by the following wry quote attributed to Arthur Eddington (1933) regarding the expanding universe:

> We walk the stage of life, performers of a drama for the benefit of the cosmic spectator. As the scenes proceed he notices that the actors are growing smaller and the action quicker. When the last act opens the curtain rises on midget actors rushing through their parts at frantic speed. Smaller and smaller. Faster and faster. One last microscopic blur of intense agitation. And then nothing.

Eddington's surreal vision accompanied a tongue-in-cheek proposal that the theory of the expanding universe might be replaced by a theory of the "shrinking atom" (1933, p. 90). It was thus a bit overdone for the sake of humor. Indeed, Eddington was not sufficiently interested in the idea to develop its implications beyond a very rudimentary level. However, it turns out that he was skirting the edges of an important duality principle.

Cosmic expansion and ordinary physical motion have something in common: they are both what might be called *ectomorphisms*. In an ectomorphism, something is mapped to, generated or replicated in something external to it. However, the Reality Principle asserts that the universe is analytically self-contained, and ectomorphism is inconsistent with self-containment. Through the principle of conspansive duality, ectomorphism is conjoined with *endomorphism*, whereby things are mapped, generated or replicated within themselves. Through conspansive endomorphism, syntactic objects are injectively mapped into their own hological interiors from their own syntactic boundaries.

In the language of TD and CF duality, this shifts the emphasis from spacetime geometry to descriptive containment, and from constructive to filtrative processing. As a result, new states are formed within the images of previous states. Nothing moves or expands "through" space; space is state, and each relocation of an object is just a move from one level of perfect stasis to another. This ties conventional motion, in which worldlines are constructively created by additions of state in Minkowski diagrams, to differential endomorphism, in which the internal descriptive potentials of attributes are cumulatively restricted.

A (Minkowski) spacetime diagram is a kind of "event lattice" in which nodes represent events and their connective worldlines represent the objects that interact in those events. The events occur at the foci of past and future light cones to which the worldlines are internal. If one could look down the time axis of such a diagram at a spacelike cross section, one would see something very much like a Venn diagram with circles corresponding to lightcone cross sections. This rotation of the diagram corresponds to conspansive dualization, converting a spatiotemporal lattice of worldlines and events to a layered series of Venn diagrams.

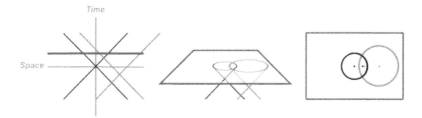

DIAGRAM XI In the above illustration, a spatial cross section of a spacetime diagram (blue line) is rotated toward the viewer and displayed along the time axis (blue rectangle). The result is a Venn diagram in which circles represent objects and events, or $(n > 1)$-ary interactive relationships of objects. That is, each circle depicts the "entangled quantum wavefunctions" of the objects which interacted with each other to generate it. The small dots in the centers of the circles represent the initial events and objects from which the circles have arisen, while the twin dots where the circles overlap reflect the fact that any possible new event, or interaction between objects involved in the old events, must occur by mutual acquisition in the intersect. The outward growth (or by conspansive duality, mutual absorption) of the circles is called *inner expansion*, while the collapse of their objects in new events is called *requantization*. The circles themselves are called IEDs, short for *inner expansive domains*, and correspond to pairs of interactive *syntactic operators* involved in generalized-perceptual events (note the hological "evacuation" and mutual absorption of the operators). Spacetime can be illustrated in terms of a layering of such Venn diagrams, mutual contact among which is referred to as "extended superposition" (in the real world, the Venn diagrams are 3-dimensional rather than planar, the circles are spheres, and "layering" is defined accordingly). Extended superposition "atemporally" distributes antecedent events over consequent events, thus putting spacetime in temporally-extended self-contact. In light of the *Telic Principle* (see below), this scenario involves a new interpretation of quantum theory, *sum over futures*. Sum over futures involves an atemporal generalization of "process", *telic recursion*, through which the universe effects on-the-fly maximization of a global self-selection parameter, *generalized utility*.

In a Venn diagram, circles represent sets through their definitive attributes. The attributes represented by the circles are synetic (syntactically distributed and homogeneous with respect to potential differences of state), and the attribute represented by a particular circle is uniformly heritable by the elements of the set represented by any circle inside it. In the spatiotemporal Venn diagram just described, the circular lightcone cross sections correspond to objects and events relating in just this way. Because quantum-scale objects are seen to exist only when they are participating in observational events, including their "generalized observations" of each other, their worldlines are merely *assumed* to exist between events and are in fact syntactically retrodicted, along with the continuum, from the last events in which they are known to have participated. This makes it possible to omit specific worldlines entirely, replacing them with series of Venn diagrams in which circles inner-expand, interpenetrate and "collapse to points" at each interactive generalized-observational event. This scenario is general, applying even to macroscopic objects consisting of many particles of matter; the higher definition of the worldlines of macroscopic objects can be imputed to a higher frequency of collapse due to interactive density among their constituent particles.

The areas inside the circles correspond to event potentials, and where events are governed by the laws of physics, to potential instantiations of physical law or "nomological syntax". Where each circle corresponds to two or more objects, it comprises object potentials as well. That is, the circular boundaries of the Venn circles can be construed as those of "potentialized" objects in the process of absorbing their spatiotemporal neighborhoods. Since the event potentials and object potentials coincide, potential instantiations of law can be said to reside "inside" the objects, and can thus be regarded as functions of their internal rules or "object syntaxes". Objects thus become syntactic operators, and events become intersections of nomological syntax in the common value of an observable state parameter, position. The circle corresponding to the new event represents an attribute consisting of all associated nomological relationships appropriate to the nature of the interaction including conserved aggregates, and forms a pointwise (statewise) "syntactic covering" for all subsequent potentials.

Notice that in this scenario, spacetime evolves linguistically rather than geometrodynamically. Although each Venn circle seems to expand continuously, its content is unchanging; its associated attribute remains static pending subsequent events involving the objects that created it. Since nothing actually changes until a new event is "substituted" for the one previous, i.e. until a new circle appears within the old one by syntactic embedment, the circles are intrinsically undefined in duration and are thus intrinsically atemporal. Time arises strictly as an ordinal relationship among circles rather than within circles themselves. With respect to time-invariant elements of syntax active in any given state (circle), the distinction between zero and nonzero duration is intrinsically meaningless; such elements are heritable under substitution and become syntactic ingredients of subsequent states. Because each circle is structurally self-distributed, nothing need be transmitted from one part of it to another; locality constraints arise only with respect to additional invariants differentially activated within circles that represent subsequent states and break the hological symmetry of their antecedents. Conspansion thus affords a certain amount of relief from problems associated with so-called "quantum nonlocality".

Because the shrinkage of an object within its prior image amounts to a form of logical substitution in which the object is Venn-diagrammatically "described" or determined by its former state, there is no way to distinguish between outward systemic expansion and inward substitution of content, or between the associated dynamical and logical "grammars". This is merely a restatement of attributive duality; topological containment relations among point-sets are equivalent to descriptively predicating truth of statements asserting containment, and on distribution relationships among state-descriptors. In conjunction with the intrinsic symmetry of externally undefined systems, attributive duality eliminates any possible logical or geometric distinction between the outward expansion of a self-contained universe as its contents remain static in size, and a logical endomorphism in which the universe remains static while the states of its contents are recursively substituted for previous states.

It has already been noted in connection with MAP that where the external dimensions of a system are undefined, no distinction as to size can be made beyond the size ratio of the system to its contents. Consider a simple arithmetical analogy: $1/2 = 1000/2000 = 1(10^{9999})/2(10^{9999}) = (\ldots)$. Where the numerator and denominator of a fraction are both multiplied by a given number, the value of the fraction does not change; it is independent of distinctions involving the size of the multiplier. Similarly, the intrinsic proportionality of a self-contained system is independent of distinctions involving any external measure. This implies that with respect to a self-contained universe for which no external measure exists, no distinction can be made between the expansion of the system with respect to its contents, and the shrinkage of its contents with respect to it. In fact, because that which is undefined cannot change – there is nothing definite with respect to which change would be possible – apparent expansion of the container cannot be extrinsically defined, but implies a conspansively-equivalent intrinsic shrinkage of its contents.

Thus, conspansive duality relates two complementary views of the universe, one based on the external (relative) states of a set of objects, and one based on the internal structures and dynamics of objects considered as language processors. The former, which depicts the universe as it is usually understood in physics and cosmology, is called ERSU, short for *Expanding Rubber Sheet Universe*, while the latter is called USRE (ERSU spelled backwards), short for *Universe as a Self-Representational Entity*. Simplistically, ERSU is like a set, specifically a topological-geometric point set, while USRE is like a self-descriptive nomological language. Whereas ERSU expands relative to the invariant sizes of its contents, USRE "conspands", holding the size of the universe invariant while allowing object sizes and time scales to shrink in mutual proportion, thus preserving general covariance.

This has certain interesting implications. First, whereas it is ordinarily assumed that the sizes of material objects remain fixed while that of the whole universe "ectomorphically" changes around them, conspansion holds the size of the universe changeless and endomorphically changes the sizes of objects. Because the universe now plays the role of invariant, there exists a global standard rate of inner expansion or mutual absorption among the contents of the universe ("c-invariance"), and due to syntactic covariance, objects must be resized or "requantized" with each new event according to a constant (time-independent) rescaling factor residing in global syntax. Second, because the rate of shrinkage is a constant function of a changing size ratio, the universe appears from an internal vantage to be accelerating in its "expansion", leading to the conspansive dual of a positive cosmological constant (Langan, 2001a).

Conspansive duality, the role of which in the CTMU is somewhat analogous to that of the Principle of Equivalence in General Relativity, is the only escape from an infinite ectomorphic "tower of turtles". Were the perceptual geometry of reality to lack a conspansive dual representation, motion of any kind would require a fixed spatial array or ectomorphic "background space" requiring an explanation of its own, and so on down the tower. Conspansion permits the universe to self-configure through temporal feedback. Each conspanding circle represents an event-potential corresponding to a certain combination of law and state; even after one of these intrinsically atemporal circles has "inner-expanded" across vast reaches of space and time, its source event is still current for anything that interacts with it, e.g. an eye catching one of its photons. At the same time, conspansion gives the quantum wave function of objects a new home: *inside the conspanding objects themselves.* Without it, the wave function not only has no home, but fails to coincide with any logically evolving system of predicates or "laws of physics". Eliminate conspansion, and reality becomes an inexplicable space full of deterministic worldlines and the weighty load of problems that can be expected when geometry is divorced from logic.

Where reality is characterized by dual-aspect infocognitive monism (read on), it consists of units of infocognition reflecting a distributed coupling of transductive syntax and informational content. Conspansion describes the "alternation" of these units between the dual (generalized-cognitive and informational) aspects of reality, and thus between syntax and state. This alternation, which permits localized mutual refinements of cognitive syntax and informational state, is essential to an evolutionary process called *telic recursion.* Telic recursion requires a further principle based on conspansive duality, the *Extended Superposition Principle*, according to which operators can be simultaneously acquired by multiple *telons*, or spatiotemporally-extensive syntax-state relationships implicating generic operators in potential events and opportunistically guiding their decoherence.

Note that conspansion explains the "arrow of time" in the sense that it is not symmetric under reversal. On the other hand, the conspansive nesting of atemporal events puts all of time in "simultaneous self-contact" without compromising ordinality. Conspansive duality can be viewed as the consequence of a type of gauge (measure) symmetry by which only the relative dimensions of the universe and its contents are important.

5.9 The Extended Superposition Principle

In quantum mechanics, *the principle of superposition of dynamical states* asserts that the possible dynamical states of a quantized system, like waves in general, can be linearly superposed, and that each dynamical state can thus be represented by a vector belonging to an abstract vector space. The superposition principle permits the definition of so-called "mixed states" consisting of many possible "pure states", or definite sets of values of state-parameters. In such a superposition, state-parameters can simultaneously have many values.

The superposition principle highlights certain problems with quantum mechanics. One problem is that quantum mechanics lacks a cogent model in which to interpret things like "mixed states" (waves alone are not sufficient). Another problem is that according to the uncertainty principle, the last states of a pair of interacting particles are generally insufficient to fully determine their next states. This, of course, raises a question: how are their next states actually determined? What is the source of the extra tie-breaking measure of determinacy required to select their next events ("collapse their wave functions")?

The answer is not, as some might suppose, "randomness"; randomness amounts to acausality, or alternatively, to informational incompressibility with respect to any distributed causal template or ingredient of causal syntax. Thus, it is either no explanation at all, or it implies the existence of a "cause" exceeding the representative capacity of distributed laws of causality. But the former is both absurd and unscientific, and the latter requires that some explicit allowance be made for higher orders of causation . . . more of an allowance than may readily be discerned in a simple, magical invocation of "randomness".

The superposition principle, like other aspects of quantum mechanics, is based on the assumption of physical *Markovianism*.[16] It refers to mixed states between adjacent

---

[16] A Markoff process is a stochastic process with no memory. That is, it is a process meeting two criteria: (1) state transitions are constrained or influenced by the present state, but not by the particular sequence of steps leading to the present state; (2) state transition contains an element of chance. Physical processes are generally assumed to meet these criteria; the laws of physics are defined in accordance with 1, and because they ultimately function on the quantum level but do not fully determine quantum state transitions, an

events, ignoring the possibility of nonrandom temporally-extensive relationships not wholly attributable to distributed laws. By putting temporally remote events in extended descriptive contact with each other, the Extended Superposition Principle enables coherent cross-temporal telic feedback and thus plays a necessary role in cosmic self-configuration. Among the higher-order determinant relationships in which events and objects can thus be implicated are utile state-syntax relationships called *telons*, telic attractors capable of guiding cosmic and biological evolution.

Given that quantum theory does not seem irrevocably attached to Markovianism, why has the possibility of higher-order causal relationships not been seriously entertained? One reason is spacetime geometry, which appears to confine objects to one-dimensional "worldlines" in which their state-transition events are separated by intervening segments that prevent them from "mixing" in any globally meaningful way. It is for this reason that superposition is usually applied only to individual state transitions, at least by those subscribing to conservative interpretations of quantum mechanics.

Conspansive duality, which incorporates TD and CF components, removes this restriction by placing state transition events in direct descriptive contact. Because the geometric intervals between events are generated and selected by descriptive processing, they no longer have separative force. Yet, since worldlines accurately reflect the distributed laws in terms of which state transitions are expressed, they are not reduced to the status of interpolated artifacts with no dynamical reality; their separative qualities are merely overridden by the state-syntax dynamic of their conspansive dual representation.

In extending the superposition concept to include nontrivial higher-order relationships, the Extended Superposition Principle opens the door to meaning and design. Because it also supports distribution relationships among states, events and syntactic strata, it makes cosmogony a distributed, coherent, ongoing event rather than a spent and discarded moment from the ancient history of the cosmos. Indeed, the usual justification for observer participation – that an observer in the present can perceptually collapse the wave functions of ancient (photon-emission) events – can be regarded as a consequence of this logical relationship.

5.10 Supertautology

Truth, a predicate representing inclusion in a domain, is the logical property by virtue of which one thing may be identified and distinguished from another at any level of resolution. All theories aim at truth, and reality theory is no exception. With respect to science, there is a problem with truth: beyond the level of direct observation, it

---

element of chance is superficially present. It is in this sense that the distributed laws of physics may be referred to as "Markovian". However, criterion 2 opens the possibility that hidden influences may be active.

cannot be certified by empirical means. To blame are various forms of uncertainty, model-theoretic ambiguity, and the problem of induction: scientific generalizations are circular insofar as they are necessarily based on the assumption that nature is uniform. The problem of induction effectively limits certitude to mathematical reasoning.

This is hardly surprising, for truth is ultimately a mathematical concept. In logic, truth is defined by means of always-true expressions called *tautologies*. A logical tautology possess three distinctive properties: it is descriptively universal, it is closed under recursive self-composition, and it is internally and externally consistent on the syntactic and semantic levels of reference. Since logic is the theory of truth, the way to construct a fully verifiable theory is to start with logic and develop the theory by means of rules or principles under which truth is heritable. Because truth is synonymous with logical tautology, this means developing the theory by adjoining rules which themselves have a tautological structure – i.e., which are universal, closed and consistent – and logically extracting the implications. A theory of reality constructed in this way is called a *supertautology*.

In a supertautological theory of reality, it is unnecessary to assume the uniformity of nature with respect to certain kinds of generalization. Instead, such generalizations can be mathematically deduced . . . e.g. nomological covariance, the invariance of the rate of global self-processing (c-invariance), and the internally-apparent accelerating expansion of the system.

5.11 Reduction and Extension

The greatest theoretical advances have typically been associated with two complementary processes, *reduction* and *extension*. The conceptual components of a theory are *reduced* to more fundamental components, and the theory *extended* by the emergence of new and more general relationships among them. The CTMU reduces reality to self-transducing information and ultimately to telesis, using the closed, reflexive syntactic structure of the former as a template for reality theory.

In science, everything requires an explanation . . . even explanations. Not only do observations demand explanatory theories, but theories require explanations of their own. Unfortunately, it is sometimes forgotten that until something has been explained in an explicable way, it has not been properly explained at all. If a theory is not self-explanatory, then it must be reduced to a more fundamental theory that explains it; otherwise, it merely relies on assumptions.

E.g., consider an explanation to the effect that "birds can fly because they have wings". Without an explanation of atmospheric resistance, this explanation is incomplete; it contains no explanation of why or how wings enable flight, merely relying on the assumption that they do. Therefore, while it is true as far as it goes, it leaves out crucial supporting knowledge and cannot stand alone. Concisely, every theory T_{i+1} that is not self-explanatory must be reducible to a more fundamental theory $T_i \vDash T_{i+1}$ that explains and supports it, so that T_i, and this explanatory regress can only end with a self-explanatory theory T_0.

This fact is very frequently forgotten in evolutionary biology, where (e.g.) details of molecular structure and dynamics are used to explain organic phenomena. Although these details come from the more fundamental theories of quantum chemistry and physics, they will never constitute a satisfactory explanation of life until they incorporate not only an explanation of physics and chemistry, but reality at large. This is true because physical (observable) reality is not a complete model for physics and thus is not self-contained with respect to explanation – in this sense, any exclusively materialistic interpretation of physical theory is *prima facie* absurd – and because physics is a non-self-explanatory theory regardless of model. To explain organic phenomena using natural selection, one needs an explanation for natural selection, including the "natural selection" of the laws of physics and the universe as a whole.

Theoretical reduction involves a regressive unbinding of progressive informational constraints in order to achieve increasingly basic explanations. Closed theoretical signatures are ripped open and reduced to more basic concepts that can be reformed into more basic and expressive signatures. However, the informational part of the regress terminates where further reduction would compromise intelligibility; there can be no further reductive regress through increasingly fundamental theoretic strata once the requirements of regression, reduction, theorization and stratification have themselves been lost. Beyond this point, infocognition gives way to informational and cognitive potential, or telesis.

The process of reducing distinctions to the homogeneous syntactic media that support them is called *syndiffeonic regression*. This process involves *unisection*, whereby the rules of structure and dynamics that respectively govern a set of distinct objects are reduced to a "syntactic join" in an infocognitive lattice of syntactic media. Unisection is a general form of reduction which implies that all properties realized within a medium are properties of the medium itself.

Where emergent properties are merely latent properties of the teleo-syntactic medium of emergence, the mysteries of emergent phenomena are reduced to just two: how are emergent properties anticipated in the syntactic structure of their medium of emergence, and why are they not expressed except under specific conditions involving (e.g.) degree of systemic complexity?

5.12 The Principle of Infocognitive Monism

Where language consists of information and information has linguistic structure, the Principle of Linguistic Reducibility implies that information is as fundamental as language. Insofar as we cannot understand reality except in theoretical (linguistic, informational) terms, this permits us to cast reality as a "self-processing language", or self-defining, self-explaining, self-modeling theory-universe ensemble, without fear of being proven wrong by some alternate theoretical reduction. However, the linguistic reduction of reality is superficially macroscopic. Just as a perfectly self-contained language must be self-processing (for lack of anything external to process it), so must the information of which it consists. This leads to the concept of *self-processing information*, and ultimately to a microscopic (quantum) theory of information.

It is easy to show that information is self-processing. Structure is attributive; the parts of any structure possess attributes that position them or otherwise define them relative to other parts. To be meaningful and thus informative, information must have structure; therefore, information must possess attributes. Attributive relationships, intrinsic or otherwise, must conform to the logical rules that govern attribution, i.e. to an attributive logical syntax incorporating the propositional and predicate calculi. So information can exist only in conjunction with attributive logical syntax. Because it necessarily incorporates attributive syntax, it has enough native self-processing capacity to maintain its intrinsic structure, which is precisely what it must do to qualify as "informational".

Because cognition and generic information transduction are identical up to isomorphism – after all, cognition is just the specific form of information processing that occurs in a mind – information processing can be described as "generalized cognition", and the coincidence of information and processor can be referred to as *infocognition*. Reality thus consists of a single "substance", infocognition, with two aspects corresponding to *transduction* and being *transduced*. Describing reality as infocognition thus amounts to (infocognitive) *dual aspect monism*. Where infocognition equals the distributed generalized self-perception and self-cognition of reality, infocognitive monism implies a stratified form of "panpsychism" in which at least three levels of self-cognition can be distinguished with respect to scope, power and coherence: *global*, *agentive* and *subordinate*.

Ultimately, the conceptual shift from information to self-transducing information requires extensions of information-intensive theories including the theories of information, computation and cybernetics. The problem stems from the fact that as it is understood in these fields, information is a limited concept based on an engineering model in which the existence of senders, receivers, messages, channels and transmissive media is already conveniently given, complete with all of the structural and dynamical laws required to make them work together. Moreover, the bit structure specified in this model relates to the actual structure of information the way propositional logic relates to logic as a whole, including the predicate calculus and model theory. To wit, only a single level of structure and functionality is considered, and attribution is primarily limited to just a pair of central predicates common to both theories, $True/False = 1/0$. Just as sentential logic concerns itself only with the functorial relationships of sentential variables and ignores their content, information theory concerns itself only with the probabilities of symbols in message strings and ignores the details of syntactic and semantic structure and processing.

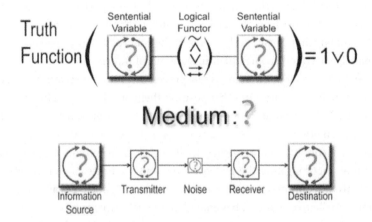

DIAGRAM XII Sentential logic and information theory both ignore entire levels of structure in order to reduce the universe to 1s and 0s. In sentential logic, sentential variables are distinguished only by whether they are true or false (1 or 0), while the standard theory of information, along with the theories of computation and cybernetics, deals with "raw data" expressed or "encoded" in the most basic possible terms, namely the binary digits 1 and 0. While the role of these "bits" is to reduce uncertainty regarding specific items of content, certain essential details of syntactic and semantic structure and processing, and more specific relationships among variables and data, are conveniently omitted. The red question marks indicate that neither sentential logic nor information theory fully explains itself, its model or its medium. [Diagram partially adapted from Shannon C. E. (1948)]

However, the most interesting part of the analogy is its logical extension. Just as sentential logic is naturally extended to encompass the levels of attribution associated with predicate logic and model theory, the theory of information can be naturally extended to encompass deeper levels of attribution . . . in fact, the same two levels adjoined to sentential logic.

Retooling the information concept consists of three steps. First, it must be equipped with the means of its own *transduction* or transformative processing. Where information transduction is (cognitively) recognized as *generalized cognition*, this amounts to replacing it with a dual-aspect quantum of reflexivity, *infocognition*, which embodies telic feedback. Second, its bit structure, a simplistic and rather uninspired blend of 2-valued propositional logic and probability theory, must be extended to accommodate logic as a whole, including (1) predicate logic, (2) model theory and (3) language theory, broadly including the theories of mathematical languages, metalanguages and generative grammars. After all, since information does nothing but attribute *linguistically*-organized *predicates* to objects in the context of *models*, its meaning involves the mathematics of predicates, languages and models. And third, it must be generalized to an ultimate ancestral medium, *telesis*, from which cognitive syntax and its informational content arise by specificative feedback as part of a unified complex . . . a recursive coupling of information and *metainformation*, or transductive syntax.

This retooling is accomplished by associating information with reflexive *syntactic operators* (units of coherent infocognition) in a reflexive linguistic structure, *Self-Configuring Self-Processing Language* (SCSPL), that incorporates its own model and is thus identical to its universe. SCSPL evolves by *conspansion* (material contraction *qua* spatial expansion), a structured grammatical alternation between a linguistic "output" phase (classical reality) consisting of the observable states or external relationships of syntactic operators, and a "production phase" that transforms one state to another.

This being said, there is a sense in which infocognitive monism well agrees with the thesis that bits are universal descriptors of reality: because the bit values 1 and 0 are analogous to the truth values of 2-valued logic, the fact that perceptual reality is described by 2-valued logic implies that it can be described in terms of bits. However, while reality at large is defined by relevance to perceptual reality in the relativistic sense, it does not consist of perceptual reality alone.

5.13 Telic Reducibility and Telic Recursion

Telic recursion is a fundamental process that tends to maximize a cosmic self-selection parameter, *generalized utility*, over a set of possible syntax-state relationships in light of the self-configurative freedom of the universe. An inherently "quantum" process that reflects the place of quantum theory in SCSPL, telic recursion is a "pre-informational" form of recursion involving a combination of hology, telic feedback and recursive selection acting on the informational potential of MU, a primal syndiffeonic form that is symmetric with respect to containment.

Where perceptual reality consists of infocognition (self-transducing information), explaining the genesis and evolution of reality amounts to explaining the genesis and evolution of infocognition. Because generalized cognition (information processing) is *temporal*, while information locates objects or message units in attributive *spaces*, information and cognition are respectively spatial and temporal in nature; infocognition is analogous to spacetime, and spacetime is infocognitive. It follows that perceptual reality consists not merely of infocognition but of spacetime, and that seeking an explanation of the genesis and evolution of reality amounts to seeking an explanation of the genesis and evolution of spacetime *qua* infocognition . . . i.e., to cosmology in the context of information transduction.

Cosmology, humanity's grand attempt to explain the origin and nature of the universe, has traditionally amounted to the search for a set of "ultimate laws" capable of explaining not only how the universe currently functions, but how it came to be. Unfortunately, even were such a set of laws to be found, the associated explanation could not be considered adequate until the laws themselves were explained, along with the fundamental objects and attributes on which they act. This gives rise to what seems like an imponderable question: how can a set of laws, objects and attributes be explained except by invoking another set of laws in the form of an explanatory syntax that would itself demand an explanation, and so on *ad infinitum*?

The answer is hiding in the question. Laws do not stand on their own, but must be defined with respect to the objects and attributes on which they act and which they accept as parameters. Similarly, objects and attributes do not stand on their own, but must be defined with respect to the rules of structure, organization and transformation that govern them. It follows that the active medium of cross-definition possesses logical primacy over laws and arguments alike, and is thus pre-informational and pre-nomological in nature . . . i.e., *telic*. *Telesis*, which can be characterized as "infocognitive potential", is the primordial active medium from which laws and their arguments and parameters emerge by mutual refinement or *telic recursion*.

In other words, telesis is a kind of "pre-spacetime" from which time and space, cognition and information, state-transitional syntax and state, have not yet separately emerged. Once bound in a primitive infocognitive form that drives emergence by generating "relievable stress" between its generalized spatial and temporal components – i.e., between state and state-transition syntax – telesis continues to be refined into new infocognitive configurations, i.e. new states and new arrangements of state-transition syntax, in order to relieve the stress between syntax and state through telic recursion (which it can never fully do, owing to the contingencies inevitably resulting from independent telic recursion on the parts of localized subsystems). As far as concerns the primitive telic-recursive infocognitive MU form itself, it does not "emerge" at all except intrinsically; it has no "external" existence except as one of the myriad possibilities that naturally exist in an unbounded realm of zero constraint.

Telic recursion occurs in two stages, *primary* and *secondary* (global and local). In the primary stage, universal (distributed) laws are formed in juxtaposition with the initial distribution of matter and energy, while the secondary stage consists of material and geometric state-transitions expressed in terms of the primary stage. That is, where universal laws are syntactic and the initial mass-energy distribution is the initial state of spacetime, secondary transitions are derived from the initial state by rules of syntax, including the laws of physics, *plus* telic recursion. The primary stage is associated with the global telor, reality as a whole; the secondary stage, with internal telors ("agent-level" observer-participants). Because there is a sense in which primary and secondary telic recursion can be regarded as "simultaneous", local telors can be said to constantly "create the universe" by channeling and actualizing generalized utility within it.

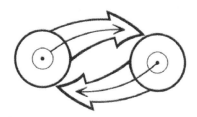

DIAGRAM XIII The above diagram illustrates the relationship of primary and secondary telic recursion, with the latter "embedded in" or expressed in terms of the former. The large circles and arrows represent universal laws (distributed syntax) engaged in telic feedback with the initial state of spacetime (initial mass-energy distribution), while the small circles and arrows represent telic feedback between localized contingent aspects of syntax and state via conspansion. The primary stage maximizes global generalized utility on an *ad hoc* basis as local telors freely and independently maximize their local utility functions. The primary-stage counterparts of inner expansion and requantization are called *coinversion* and *incoversion*. It is by virtue of telic recursion that the SCSPL universe can be described as its own self-simulative, self-actualizative "quantum protocomputer".

Deterministic computational and continuum models of reality are recursive in the standard sense; they evolve by recurrent operations on state from a closed set of "rules" or "laws". Because the laws are invariant and act deterministically on a static discrete array or continuum, there exists neither the room nor the means for optimization, and no room for self-design. The CTMU, on the other hand, is conspansive and telic-recursive; because new state-potentials are constantly being created by evacuation and mutual absorption of coherent objects (syntactic operators) through conspansion, metrical and nomological uncertainty prevail wherever standard recursion is impaired by object sparsity. This amounts to self-generative freedom, hologically providing reality with a "self-simulative scratchpad" on which to compare the aggregate utility of multiple self-configurations for self-optimizative purposes.

Standard recursion is "Markovian" in that when a recursive function is executed, each successive recursion is applied to the result of the preceding one. Telic recursion is more than Markovian; it self-actualizatively coordinates events in light of higher-order relationships or *telons* that are invariant with respect to overall identity, but may display some degree of polymorphism on lower orders. Once one of these relationships is nucleated by an opportunity for telic recursion, it can become an ingredient of syntax in one or more telic-recursive (global or agent-level) operators or *telors* and be "carried outward" by inner expansion, i.e. sustained within the operator as it engages in mutual absorption with other operators. Two features of conspansive spacetime, the atemporal homogeneity of IEDs (operator strata) and the possibility of extended superposition, then permit the telon to self-actualize by "intelligently", i.e. telic-recursively, coordinating events in such a way as to bring about its own emergence (subject to various more or less subtle restrictions involving available freedom, noise and competitive interference from other telons). In any self-contained, self-determinative system, telic recursion is integral to the cosmic, teleo-biological and volitional (Langan, 2002a) levels of evolution.

5.14 The Telic Principle

Restricted to the teleological ("Why?") level of explanation, MAP yields the *Telic Principle*: the universe configures itself according to the requirement that it self-select from a background of undifferentiated ontological potential or *telesis*. This requirement, amounting to a need for *self-actualization* and *self-expression*, is implicit in the MU form. The Telic Principle is responsible for converting potential to actuality in such a way as to maximize a universal self-selection parameter, *generalized utility*.

Teleology, the idea that the universe has a purpose which explains its existence and guides its evolution, some time ago began losing sway in the court of scientific opinion. Although it was at first assumed that a more neutral, less "theological" explanation for the existence of man and the universe would come along to fill the resulting explanatory void, it eventually became evident that no such replacement was conveniently falling out of the equations; some amount of higher-level interpretation would be required in any case. This marked the rise of the so-called *Anthropic Principle*, which now comes in several flavors including "weak", "strong", "final", and that favored by Wheeler, "participatory".

The initial (weak) version, the *Weak Anthropic Principle* or WAP, begins with the trivial if somewhat Bayesian point that our cosmological observations of the universe reveal a capacity for life "because" a life-bearing universe is the only kind of universe in which there are living beings able to make cosmological observations. But while this seems to imply that there exists a domain of many universes in which such a universe can be passively distinguished by the circumstantial constraint that it contain living observers, the WAP offers no ready explanation for such a domain. Indeed, to those not convinced of its virtues, the WAP almost seems to add an unnecessary dose of explanatory red ink to the cosmological ledger.

The *Strong Anthropic Principle* (SAP) eliminates much of this red ink by making a more extreme claim, asserting that the existence of intelligent life is not just a circumstantial selection principle, but a *sine qua non* of cosmic existence. In effect, this limits the set of possible universes to just those which are capable of producing life. However, this leads to problems. How can the idea that living observers are necessary for the existence of the universe be squared with the idea that objective reality is essentially independent of observation and those who observe it? And how does intelligent life, which seems to have evolved billions of years after the universe was born, play any kind of causal role in cosmology? Is some sort of "time travel" occurring? Selection is one thing; retroactive self-generation is quite another.

It has often been remarked that the anthropic principles employ circular reasoning. I.e., they seem to take that which they purport to explain, the observable fact that the universe is "fine-tuned" to support life, as a premise, asserting that living beings observe the universe to be friendly to life "because" life is present in the universe to make this observation. In other words, we are here to observe the universe, and the universe is here to let us observe it, because we are here to observe the universe! Unfortunately, the anthropic principles lack something that they would need to make this work: a circular model to which their loop-like reasoning can be consistently mapped. Quite simply, the type of causal circularity they suggest is at odds with the "arrow of time" and other aspects of the prevailing non-circular models of time and space.

Because circular arguments are self-justifying and resistant to falsification, it is frequently assumed that tautology and circular reasoning are absolute theoretical evils. But this is far from the case, for logic and mathematics are almost completely based on circularity. Truth and logical tautology, recursion and iteration, algebraic and topological closure . . . all involve it to some degree. The problems arise only when circular reasoning is employed without the assurance of full mathematical generality, incorporating false claims of universality on (what may be) non-universal premises.

Unfortunately, not even valid tautologies are embraced by the prevailing school of scientific philosophy, falsificationism. While non-universal tautologies are rightly forbidden due to their resistance to falsificative procedures that would reveal their limitations, universal tautologies are pronounced "scientifically uninteresting" for much the same reason. But in fact, science could exist in no way, shape or form without them. The very possibility of a scientific observation is utterly dependent on the existence of tautological forms on which to base a stable, invariant syntax of perception. This raises the possibility that falsificationist thinking has accidentally obscured the true place of tautological reasoning in cosmology.

If the universe is really circular enough to support some form of "anthropic" argument, its circularity must be defined and built into its structure in a logical and therefore universal and necessary way. The Telic principle simply asserts that this is the case;

the most fundamental imperative of reality is such as to force on it a supertautological, conspansive structure. Thus, the universe "selects itself" from *unbound telesis* or UBT, a realm of zero information and unlimited ontological potential, by means of *telic recursion*, whereby infocognitive syntax and its informational content are cross-refined through telic (syntax-state) feedback over the entire range of potential syntax-state relationships, up to and including all of spacetime and reality in general.

The Telic Principle differs from anthropic principles in several important ways. First, it is accompanied by supporting principles and models which show that the universe possesses the necessary degree of circularity, particularly with respect to time. In particular, the Extended Superposition Principle, a property of conspansive spacetime that coherently relates widely-separated events, lets the universe "retrodict" itself through meaningful cross-temporal feedback. Moreover, in order to function as a selection principle, it generates a generalized global selection parameter analogous to "self-utility", which it then seeks to maximize in light of the evolutionary freedom of the cosmos as expressed through localized telic subsystems which mirror the overall system in seeking to maximize (local) utility. In this respect, the Telic Principle is an ontological extension of so-called "principles of economy" like those of Maupertuis and Hamilton regarding least action, replacing least action with deviation from generalized utility.

In keeping with its clear teleological import, the Telic Principle is not without what might be described as theological ramifications. For example, certain properties of the reflexive, self-contained language of reality – that it is syntactically self-distributed, self-reading, and coherently self-configuring and self-processing – respectively correspond to the traditional theological properties *omnipresence, omniscience* and *omnipotence*. While the kind of theology that this entails neither requires nor supports the intercession of any "supernatural" being external to the real universe itself, it does support the existence of a supraphysical being (the SCSPL global operator-designer) capable of bringing more to bear on localized physical contexts than meets the casual eye. And because the physical (directly observable) part of reality is logically inadequate to explain its own genesis, maintenance, evolution or consistency, it alone is incapable of properly containing the being in question.

6 Some Background

A review of the standard computational theory of language may prove useful. Computation theory recognizes two general types of automata, transducers and acceptors. Transducers convert input to output, while acceptors classify or "recognize" input consisting of strings of symbols without necessarily producing output.

A *finite transducer* is a 5-tuple $(\Sigma, Q, \Gamma, \delta, \omega)$ where Σ is a finite nonempty input alphabet, Q is a finite nonempty state set, Γ is a finite nonempty output alphabet, $\delta : Q \times \Sigma \to Q$ is the state transition function, and $\omega : Q \times \Sigma \to \Gamma$ is the output function. To this we can add a start state q_0. Finite transducers ultimately rely on mechanical laws to function, transforming informational input to informational output by transforming their own states.

A *finite acceptor* is a 5-tuple $(Q, \Sigma, \delta, q_0, A)$, where Q is a nonempty finite set of internal states, and Σ is an alphabet, q_0, is the start state, and $A \subseteq Q$ is the set of accepting states. The range of the transition mapping δ determines the type of acceptor; it is *deterministic* if $\delta : Q \times \Sigma \to Q$, and *nondeterministic* if $\delta : Q \times \Sigma \to 2^Q$ (where 2^Q represents the power set of possible states). A deterministic finite acceptor $(Q, \Sigma, \delta, q_0, A)$ *accepts* a string $x \in \Sigma^*$ iff $\delta(q_0, x) \in A$. A *language* is the set of strings accepted by a given automaton or class of automata.

Languages are generated by grammars. In the computational theory of language, a generative (or phrase structure) grammar G is a 4-tuple (N, T, P, σ) consisting of:

(1) a finite set N of *nonterminals*;

(2) a finite nonempty set T of *terminals*, with $N \cap T = \varnothing$ and $N \cup T = A$ (the total *alphabet* of the grammar);

(3) a finite set of productions $P \subset ((N \cup T)^* \setminus T^*) \times (N \cup T)^*$ consisting of nonterminal arguments and their possibly terminal transforms;

(4) an element σ of N called the *starting symbol*.

The implementation of such a grammar is a deductive process leading from the general to the specific; starting from the most general symbol σ (which stands for "sentence"), increasingly specific productions lead to a terminal configuration. The production (x, y), often written $x \to y$, signifies replacement of x by y, or equivalently, the *substitution* of y for x. Where A^* denotes the set of all strings or "words" in A, and $A^* \setminus T^*$ denotes the complement of T^* in A^*, a word $w \in (A^* \setminus T^*)$ *generates* another word w' if $w = w_1 X w_2$, $w' = w_1 X' w_2$, and $X \to X'$ is a production.

The theory of generative grammars classifies them according to the least powerful acceptor that can recognize the languages they generate. Type 0 grammars generate unrestricted languages requiring a universal computer (Turing machine) with unlimited memory; type 1 grammars generate context-sensitive languages requiring a linear-bounded automaton with memory proportional to word length; type 2 grammars generate context-free languages requiring a pushdown automaton with a memory stack in which a fixed number of elements are available at any point; and type 3 grammars generate regular languages requiring a finite deterministic automaton with no memory.

There is an obvious parallel between the states and state transitions of automata, and the strings and productions of a grammar. An automaton processes input strings through its internal states, expressing them in terms of its own "internal language". Indeed, a physical automaton in the act of processing an input string can be seen as a dynamic linguistic stratification incorporating the input language, the mutable programming of the automaton (including assembly and machine code), its hard-wired architecture, the nomological language consisting of the laws of physics according to which the hardware functions, and any "metaphysical" level of language necessary to define and maintain the laws of physics themselves. Since each language in this sequence is expressed in terms of the next one after it, the languages form a "descriptive nesting" in which the syntax of each distributes over all of those preceding it.

The *syntax* of a language consists of its grammar and the structure of its expressions. That is, a syntax is a compilation of the spatial (structural) and temporal (grammatical, transformational) rules of the associated language; its rules are invariant, general, and distributive with respect to the entire set of expressions comprising the language. This concept is as meaningful for automata as it is for the languages they process, applying to every level of the linguistic stratification just described. For example, where the concept of general covariance expresses the general and distributive nature of the laws of physics, these laws can be regarded as a "syntax" unto themselves, and so can the more general mathematical laws applying to the various mathematical structures to which the laws of physics implicitly refer.

Physics and mathematics are usually viewed not as languages, but as theories. Even though they are necessarily expressed in terms of language, they are usually considered "more specific". But like automata, they too meet linguistic criteria. For instance, mathematical theories have syntaxes consisting of axioms and rules of inference, and various derived expressions such as definitions, theorems and corollaries. More generally, a theory is simply an informational construct that plays a direct definitive, descriptive or explanatory role with respect to something that needs to be defined, described or explained. Because theories consist of recognizable strings of symbols taking the form of statements and equations and obey "syntaxes" consisting of axioms, principles, hunches or rules of thumb, and in fact share their syntaxes with the objects of theorization up to descriptive isomorphism, they are languages. Indeed, the very requisites of theorization, namely perception and cognition, are languages in the sense that they consist of sensory or conceptual "expressions" and conform to logical and nonlogical syntaxes consisting of general rules of structure and operation, including (but not necessarily limited to) the physical structures and dynamics of our brains and nervous systems.

Let us quickly review some of the technical details of theoretical languages. A mathematical theory consists of propositions containing basic predicates and functions representing fundamental concepts. For example, set theory is based on the concept of *membership* ($\in$); geometry is strongly dependent on primitive concepts like *angle* and *distance*; and elementary arithmetic incorporates the more or less basic concepts of *addition, multiplication* and *order* ($<$). The symbols that stand for these concepts, sometimes called *nonlogical constants*, form the signature Σ of the theory. This signature includes symbols for relations, functions and individuals, each with an "arity" or valence. Beyond its signature, a mathematical theory contains *variables* (preassigned symbols denoting objects from a previously specified domain) for individuals represented by symbols like $(x, y, z, \ldots)$, logical symbols (logical constants) like $(\sim, \wedge, \vee, \rightarrow, \leftrightarrow, =, \exists, \forall)$, and auxiliary technical symbols (Gellert et al., 1977).

An *elementary language* L_Σ (language of the predicate calculus) can be defined as a set of expressions or propositional forms incorporating these logical and nonlogical symbols and their syntactic rules. The terms of L_Σ are defined as follows:

(1)   variables and constants for individuals are terms;

(2)   if F is an n-ary function symbol and $t_1, \ldots, t_n$ are terms, then $Ft_1, \ldots, t_n$ is a term;

(3)   a sequence of symbols is a term *iff* it conforms to 1 and 2.

The expressions of L_Σ are characterized thusly:

(1)   Where R is an n-ary function symbol and $t_1, \ldots, t_n$ are terms, then $Rt_1, \ldots, t_n$ is an *atomic expression* (i.e., an instance of attribution);

(2)   If A and B are expressions, then so are $\sim A$, $(A \wedge B)$, $(A \vee B)$, $(A \rightarrow B)$, and $(A \leftrightarrow B)$;

(3)   If $A(x)$ is an expression containing the variable x, but not $\exists x$ or $\forall x$, then so are $\exists x A(x)$ and $\forall x A(x)$;

(4)   A sequence of symbols is an expression only if formed in accordance with 1-3.

By nature, the languages of predicate logic are descriptive; their expressions describe relationships holding within various mathematical structures.[17]

It should now be clear that in order to define a theoretical language, one simply creates a syntax for it by extending the syntax of logic to accommodate the spatial and temporal relationships necessarily holding among its nonlogical constants under all

---

[17] Not all expressions are propositions; propositions are expressions with no free (unquantified) variables. Permitting the quantification of unary (one-place) predicates and treating them as individuals results in a generalization of the elementary languages to a more expressive class of languages, the monadic languages of the second order. Further generalizations are possible along these lines.

(or at least most) logical circumstances within the intended scope of the theory. Like the syntax of logic itself, which is a theory of descriptive inclusion or "truth" based on the cognitive and perceptual need to distinguish *that which is* from *that which is not*, the syntax of a theoretical language is also based on ingredients and imperatives of cognitive and perceptual reality. We have already remarked on the equivalence of automata and languages; the states and state transitions of automata parallel the strings and productions of a grammar. To find the theoretical language describing any class of tranducers, we need merely adjoin to the syntax of logic the nonlogical descriptors of their transductive structures and processes.

The primary transducers of the overall language of science are scientists, and their transductive syntax consists of the syntax of generalized scientific observation and theorization, i.e. perception and cognition. We may therefore partition or stratify this syntax according to the nature of the logical and nonlogical elements incorporated in syntactic rules. For example, we might develop four classes corresponding to the fundamental trio *space, time* and *object*, a class containing the rules of logic and mathematics, a class consisting of the perceptual qualia in terms of which we define and extract experience, meaning and utility from perceptual and cognitive reality, and a class accounting for more nebulous feelings and emotions integral to the determination of utility for qualic relationships.[18] For now, we might as well call these classes STOS, LMS, QPS and ETS, respectively standing for *space-time-object syntax, logico-mathematical syntax, qualio-perceptual syntax*, and *emo-telic syntax*, along with a high-level interrelationship of these components to the structure of which all or some of them ultimately contribute. Together, these ingredients comprise the Human Cognitive-Perceptual Syntax or HCS.[19]

As every language user is aware, there is more to language processing than recognition and transduction. There is also *communication*. The concepts of language and communication are inseparable; languages are abstract structures through which communication is effected, and communication involves exchange of input and output by language users. Any time we have a syntax, a set of representative expressions

---

[18] Lest the inclusion of utility, qualia or feelings seem "unscientific", we need merely observe that it would be vastly more unscientific to ignore things that are subjectively known to exist on the wishful and rationally unjustifiable assumption that subjectivity and subjective predicates play no part in the self-definition of reality. Insofar as subjectivity merely refers to the coherent intrinsic identities of the elements of objective relationships, this would be logically absurd. But in any case, our aim at this point is merely to classify the basic elements in terms of which we view the world, whether or not they have thus far proven accessible to standard empirical methodology, and this means recognizing the reality of qualic and emotional predicates and adjoining the corresponding nonlogical constants to SCSPL syntax. If QPS and ETS predicates turn out to be reducible to more fundamental STOS/LMS predicates, then very well; it will permit a convenient reduction of the syntax. But this is certainly not something that can be decided in advance.

[19] Cognitive-perceptual syntax consists of (1) sets, posets or tosets of attributes (telons), (2) perceptual rules of external attribution for mapping external relationships into telons, (3) cognitive rules of internal attribution for cognitive (internal, non-perceptual) state-transition, and (4) laws of dependency and conjugacy according to which perceptual or cognitive rules of external or internal attribution may or may not act in a particular order or in simultaneity.

conforming to it, and a set of language processors, we have a language and the possibility of meaningful communication among its processors. Where communication conveys information and information represents relationships, communication is about more than just the states of communicators; it can carry any information representing any kind of relationship. Accordingly, communicators not only accept and transduce language, but use it to represent to each other their views of the world.

The communication paradigm is perfectly general and holds on all scales. It applies not merely on the level of expressions exchanged by communicators, but even on the level of basic status information exchanged by the interactive processing elements of an automaton. That is, language processing itself can be regarded as a form of communication; in order to actualize a language through some form of processing, it must be intersected with a processing system that functions through operational communication among its parts. A universal machine, for example, is a "self-communication system" relaying information among its abstract components (indeed, communication is the very embodiment of the three basic operations of a universal computer, namely *read, write* and *relocation*). The structural and dynamical rules of language processors thus correspond directly to the syntaxes of languages; both kinds of system evolve by communicative intersection of syntax and state (or content). It follows that languages and automata can be treated on a par, and that since automata can be treated as self-communication systems, so can languages.

In the technical descriptions of automata and languages outlined above, a certain model of the world is implicit. Automata accept input from the outside world, transform it through their internal states, and (sometimes) return the result to the outside world when they are finished. Language and information are either *inside* or *outside* the automata, and they are inside only part of the time. The rest of the time, the information is presumably either lying around someplace else in the environment or en route from one place to another. But where communication happens on all scales, the distinction between *inside* and *outside* is not so clear. The languages communicated among language users and processors, and the languages embodied by users and processors themselves, occupy an overall medium with a unified communicative syntax largely indifferent to the distinction.

The laws that govern a system may be reposed in the space that contains its objects, or in the objects themselves. Classical physics reposes everything in space, applying spatial concepts like vectors and tensors to fields outside the objects. However, it is possible to apply a logical transformation which inverts this picture, turning it "outside-in". This results in a "distributed subjectivization" in which everything occurs *inside* the objects; the objects are simply defined to consistently internalize their interactions, effectively putting every object "inside" every other one in a generalized way and thereby placing the *contents* of space on the same footing as that formerly occupied by the containing space itself. Vectors and tensors then become descriptors of the internal syntactic properties and states of objects. In effect, the universe becomes a "self-simulation" running *inside* its own contents.

This view, which is complementary to the conventional geometric one, is called *transductive algebra*. The "dual" relationship between geometry and transductive algebra is called *conspansive duality*. In conjunction with other principles including hology and SCSPL-infocognitive-telic reducibility, conspansive duality can afford fresh insight on the nature of reality and the physical world. One simply takes the conventional picture, turns it outside-in, puts the two pictures together, and extracts the implications. The relationship of this new picture to the old one is extensional rather than competitive, embedding the geometric model in a larger and more complete conspansive model uniting it with its dual model. In any case, all equivalent models are on an equal footing, and the only scientific hypotheses on which doubt could be shed as a result of this extension are those based on the fallacious assumption that the geometric model is the "whole story".

7 Introduction to SCSPL

According to the Reality Principle, the universe is self contained, and according to infocognitive monism, it regresses to a realm of nil constraint (*unbound telesis* or UBT) from which it must refine itself. According to the Telic Principle, which states that the universe must provide itself with the means to do this, it must make and realize its own "choice to exist"; by reason of its absolute priority, this act of choice is identical to that which is chosen, i.e. the universe itself, and thus reflexive. I.e., "existence is everywhere the choice to exist." Accordingly, the universe must adopt a reflexive form in which it can "select itself" for self-defined existence, with the selection function identical to that which is selected. This means that it must take a certain general or "initial" form, the *MU form*, which contains all of the requisites for generating the contents of reality. Due to hology, whereby the self-contained universe has nothing but itself of which to consist, this form is self-distributed.

One might at first be tempted to object that there is no reason to believe that the universe does not simply "exist", and thus that self-selection is unnecessary. However, this is not a valid position. First, it involves a more or less subtle appeal to something external to the universe, namely a prior / external informational medium or "syntax" of existence; if such a syntax were sufficiently relevant to this reality, i.e. sufficiently real, to support its existence, then it would be analytically included in reality (as defined up to perceptual relevance). Second, active self-selection is indeed necessary, for existence is not merely a state but a process; the universe must internally distinguish *that which it is* from *that which it is not*, and passivity is ruled out because it would again imply the involvement of a complementary active principle of external origin.

By the Principle of Linguistic Reducibility, reality is a language. Because it is self-contained with respect to processing as well as configuration, it is a *Self-Configuring Self-Processing Language* or SCSPL whose general spatiotemporal structure is hologically replicated everywhere within it as self-transductive syntax. This reduces the generative phase of reality, including physical cosmogony, to the generative grammar of SCSPL. This reality-generative grammar is called Γ *grammar* and the MU form, being the most general or prior form of reality, is its basis. By the Principle of Infocognitive Monism and the hology of MU, SCSPL consists of MU-configured infocognition, and Γ grammar describes the generation and transformation of this universal constituent.

SCSPL is not an ordinary language, and Γ grammar is not an ordinary generative grammar. The reasons come down to the inherent limitations of computational language theory. In standard computation theory, a language consists of the set of strings accepted by a given automaton or class of automata; e.g., a language L is called "regular" if there is a finite-state automaton that accepts it. However, this approach is inadequate for SCSPL. First, it centers on *computation*, a general type of information processing associated with an abstract automaton, the Turing machine or "universal computer", that could never have generated the informational structure of the real universe. Being an informational and metainformational (syntactic) construct, the universal computer can itself account for the genesis of neither syntax nor information. Second, unlike ordinary languages, the reality-language cannot rely on an external mind or automaton or preexisting hardware substrate for recognition and processing. Since any processor real enough to recognize and process reality is necessarily a *part* of reality, the language-processor distinction is without ontological force.

Thus, while ordinary discrete models of reality rely heavily on the language-processor distinction, SCSPL incurs no such debt. For example, cellular automaton models typically distinguish between a spatial array, the informational objects existing therein, and the distributed set of temporal state-transition rules by which the array and its contents are regulated. In contrast, SCSPL regards language and processor as aspects of an underlying infocognitive unity. By conspansive (ectomorphism-endomorphism) duality, SCSPL objects contain space and time in as real a sense as that in which spacetime contains the objects, resulting in a partial identification of space, time and matter. SCSPL is more than a reflexive programming language endowed with the capacity for computational self-execution; it is a protocomputational entity capable of telic recursion, and thus of generating its own informational and syntactic structure and dynamics.

Whereas ordinary computational models are informational and syntactic in character, the protocomputational nature of SCSPL requires a generalization of information and syntax. With respect to the origin or ultimate nature of perceptual reality, explanation is a reductive/inductive process that regressively unbinds constraints in order to lay bare those of highest priority and generality. This process eventually leads to the most basic intelligible descriptor that can be formulated, beyond which lies only the unintelligible. This marks the transition from information and syntax to a convergent reductive generalization, *telesis.*[20]

This points to a universal property of language: it is dynamic. While it is often conveniently assumed that languages are timeless Platonic ideals that waft around waiting to be processed by external acceptors, they can be treated in terms of static information only by users or processors that provide them with an external transductive syntax, and only then by neglecting certain underlying necessities. For example, to physically realize the informational structure of a language in a printed or electronic medium, it

---

[20] To see how information can be beneficially reduced when all but information is uninformative by definition, one need merely recognize that information is not a stand-alone proposition; it is never found apart from syntax. Indeed, it is only by syntactic acquisition that anything is ever "found" at all. That which is recognizable only as syntactic content requires syntactic containment, becoming meaningful only as acquired by a syntactic operator able to sustain its relational structure; without attributive transduction, a bit of information has nothing to quantify. This implies that information can be generalized in terms of "what it has in common with syntax", namely the syndiffeonic relationship between information and syntax.

must be expressed in terms of physical particles that dynamically recognize each other's locations to the extent required to maintain the spatial relationships comprising its informational structure. This is a general requirement, extending from the physical and concrete to the mathematical and abstract.

Thus, languages are ultimately self-processing; they must either contain their processors in their expressions, or be expressed in terms of a more basic language fulfilling this requirement. Accordingly, the expressions of SCSPL are dynamic informational configurations of information-processors, implying that SCSPL everywhere consists of information and acceptive-transductive syntax in a state of logical intersection. Together, information and syntax comprise *infocognition*, self-transducing information in the form of SCSPL *syntactic operators* that cross-absorptively "communicate" by acquiring each other's informational states as cognitive-syntactic content. It is to the common basis of these two components that information may be reduced in the SCSPL context. Where the term *telesis* denotes this common component of information and syntax, SCSPL grammar refines infocognition by binding or constraining telesis as infocognition.

To the extent that any grammar functions by the recursive application of syntactic rules, SCSPL grammar is recursive ("self-calling"). However, SCSPL grammar is not merely deterministically or nondeterministically recursive, but telic-recursive. While an ordinary grammar recursively processes information or binds informational potential to an invariant syntax that distributes over its products, Γ grammar binds *telesis*, infocognitive potential ranging over possible relationships of syntax and state, by cross-refining syntax and its informational content through telic recursion. Telic recursion is the process responsible for configuring the syntax-content relationships on which standard informational recursion is based; its existence is an ontological requirement of reality. The telic-recursive cross-refinement of syntax and content is implicit in the "seed" of Γ grammar, the MU form, which embodies the potential for perfect complementarity of syntax and state, law and matter.

Since this potential can only be specifically realized through the infocognitive binding of telesis, and localized telic binding is freely and independently effected by localized, mutually decoherent telic operators, deviations from perfect complementarity are ubiquitous. SCSPL evolution, which can be viewed as an attempt to help this complementarity emerge from its potential status in MU, incorporates a global (syntactic) invariant that works to minimize the total deviation from perfect complementarity of syntax and state as syntactic operators freely and independently bind telesis. This primary SCSPL invariant, the *Telic Principle*, takes the form of a selection function with a quantitative parameter, *generalized utility*, related to the deviation. The Telic Principle can be regarded as the primary component of SCSPL syntax . . . the spatiotemporally distributed self-selective "choice to exist" coinciding with MU.

SCSPL incorporates the concepts of syntactic stratification and syntactic distribution. For example, because the laws of mathematics everywhere apply with respect to the laws of physics, the former distribute over the latter in the syntactic sense. Thus, where the laws of mathematics and physics are denoted by S1=LMS and S2 respectively, S1 *distributes over* S2, i.e. forms a *syntactic covering* for S2. Essentially, this means that the laws of mathematics are everywhere a required syntactic component of the language of physics. With S2 is associated an SCSPL "sublanguage" called L_O (with a letter O subscript). L_O constitutes the world of perception, the classical objective universe of sense data traditionally studied by science. L_O is contained in the telic-recursive, pre-informational phase of SCSPL, L_S, which encompasses the cross-refinement of L_O syntax and L_O content from the pre-infocognitive aspect of SCSPL. The part of SCSPL grammar confined to L_O incorporates certain restrictions to which L_S is not subject; e.g., the grammatical portion of L_O (S2) is fixed, distributed and supposedly continuous, while that of L_S can also be mutable, local and discrete . . . in a word, telic.

Γ grammar is the generative grammar of SCSPL = ($L_S \supset L_O$). Γ grammar is unlike an ordinary grammar in that its processors, products and productions coincide and are mutually formed by telic recursion. Syntax and state, loosely analogous to *form* and *content* (or *productions* and *products*), are mutually refined from telesis through telic recursion by infocognitive processors. Production rules include the Telic Principle, distributed elements of syntax formed in the primary phase of telic recursion, and more or less polymorphic telons formed by agent-level telors. The corresponding modes of production are global telic recursion, informational recursion by distributed syntax, and local telic recursion.

The "words" produced by Γ grammar are not strings of symbols, but L_O spatial relationships among parallel processors that can read and write to each other's states. In effect, the states of its processors are roughly analogous to the symbols and strings of an ordinary language. The processors of Γ grammar thus function not only as transducers but as symbolic placeholders for observables and values, while their external states correspond to products and their state transitions realize the productions of the grammar. In other words, the states and state transitions of the processors of Γ grammar comprise a representation of Γ grammar, rendering SCSPL a dynamic self-modeling language or "interactive self-simulation".

In the following description, products are limited to the physical end products associated with L_O. This is in no way to be interpreted to mean that the only SCSPL products are physical products; in fact, everything in SCSPL is to some extent a telic-recursive "product" of everything else. However, where the primary explanandum is physical (scientifically observable) reality, L_O is an appropriate choice.

$\Gamma = (O, R, P, \mu)$ contains:

(1) A set O of active reflexive objects including Γ itself, the *processors* (producers-reducers)[21] of Γ. All processors are capable of and responsive to informational (deterministic) recursion. O includes a distinguished set $\Sigma = \{\Gamma, A, Q\}$ of *syntactic operators*, coherent processors capable of or responsive to telic recursion. In general, the parts of SCSPL syntax active within a given operator depend on its specific type. Σ includes the global processor Γ, the set $Q = \{q_i\}$ of reducible and irreducible stable particles that are responsive to telic recursion in a degree proportional to their freedom and coherence, and the set A of telic *agents*, active telic-recursive operators or *telors* capable of expressing teleology on the local level. Elements of A need not occupy L_O, but may exist in L_S. Where υ denotes the generalized self-selection parameter of Γ, the elements of A are required by Γ as internal υ-responsive "sensor-controllers".

(2) A set $R = (R_O, R_S)$ of products containing a subset $R_O = (\sigma_O, \tau_O, \pi_O)$ of L_O *product states* including all of the relations of L_O, and a subset R_S of *telons* or "pre-products" generated in L_S by telic recursion associated with global or agent-level syntactic operators. The elements of σ_O are *spatial* relations, those of τ_O are *temporal* relations, and those of π_O are *spatiotemporal* relations containing both σ_O and τ_O relations. σ_O consists of relations of states regarding which the corresponding transducers have no mutual input; τ_O consists of sequences of consecutive states of single objects; and π_O consists of *processes*, or combinations of both. These states are not in general fully determined by L_O rules of state transformation, but require telic augmentation for actualization.

(3) A set $P = (N, T)$ consisting of the *productions* of Γ. N consists of the distributed descriptors of π_O, including the spatiotemporally-distributed Markovian and conservative descriptors called "laws of physics", while T consists of active L_S entities analogous to those of N but associated with specific telons (pre-products) from R_S and subject to coordinated local variation in the context of higher-order telonic relationships. The elements of N are determined in the primary stage of telic recursion, while those of T are determined in the secondary stage of telic recursion.

(4) A starting configuration, the *MU form* μ, which is identical to the telic recursion event which creates it (the inception of SCSPL and Γ grammar is a telic recursion, not an informational-algorithmic recursion). It is this identity of event and outcome that determines the innate spatial and temporal characteristics of spacetime, for which μ is the "seed". The MU form can be regarded as an "intrinsic perturbation" or "intrinsic asymmetry" in UBT. The MU form is distributed over SCSPL.

---

[21] For present purposes, reduction may be understood as reverse production. As such, it is essential to grammatical recognition.

A processor of a grammar G is any natural or artificial dynamical system that operates, changes state or processes information in conformance to the rules of G. Unlike ordinary generative grammars, Γ grammar requires no external processors; its processors and productions are identical. Thus, Γ grammar is executed by its own productions in levels of syntactic distribution ranging from the global to the object level. In fact, O, R and P – processors, products (states) and production events – all coincide and thus exhibit a form of triality. This three-way coincidence is characteristic of Γ grammar and captures many of its essential features.

O-R-P coincidence is already to some extent realized in the standard language-grammar-processor model of computation theory, but only inadvertently. While linguistic processing is dynamically paralleled by changes in the internal and external states of processors, the processors are still considered separate from the language and grammar being processed. Moreover, the basic medium of processing is not considered, the model is not self-sufficient, and recursion is merely informational and computational; there is no allowance for infocognition or telic recursion. SCSPL shares none of these limitations.

Γ grammar generates SCSPL according to the utility of its sentient processors, including the self-utility of Γ and the utility of its L_O relations to telors in A. Γ and A generate telons on the global and local level respectively; thus, they must be capable of recognizing and maximizing the selection parameter υ (in the case of human telors, for example, this requires the QPS and ETS components of the HCS). As such, they are responsible for telic recursion and may be regarded as the "generators" of Γ grammar, while the set Q of elementary physical objects are freely and competitively acquired by telons and thus occupy an ontologically secondary position.

Γ grammar is conspansive. Non-global processors alternate between the generation and selective actualization of possible productions, and thus between the generative and selective (inner expansive and requantizative) phases of conspansion. The selective phase of an operator coincides with interactive mutual-acquisition events, while the generative phase coincides with the generation and selective actualization of possible productions through hological multiplexing. In conjunction with extended spatiotemporal superposition, conspansion provides the means of local (telic and informational) recursion.

Conspansion is a global process which cannot be locally differentiated as to rate. Its rate is thus a globally invariant "time-space conversion factor", and because all changes of local state must be expressed in terms of it, it is maximal. This invariant maximal rate of production is referred to as the *rate of conspansion* c and can be physically identified with the speed of light *in vacuo*.[22] The implications of the constancy of c and N in

---

[22] Because the propagation of light is a conspansion-dependent phenomenon, c cannot be affected by impedance or manipulation of photons.

light of MAP have already been noted with respect to internally-apparent accelerating expansion of the global operator.

It is instructive to experiment with the various constructions that may be placed on L_S and L_O. For example, one can think of L_S as "L-sim", reflecting its self-simulative, telic-recursive aspect, and of L_O as "L-out", the output of this self-simulation. One can associate L_O with observable states and distributed-deterministic state-transition syntax, and L_S with the metasyntactic Telic Principle. One can even think of L_S and L_O as respectively *internal* and (partially) *external* to SCSPL syntactic operators, and thus as loosely correspondent to the *subjective* and *objective* aspects of reality. Where L_S and L_O are associated with the coherent inner expansion and decoherent requantization phases of conspansion, so then are subjective and objective reality, simulation and output, "wave and particle". In other words, the subjective-objective distinction, along with complementarity, can be viewed as functions of conspansive duality.

The fact that L_O has a foliated structure consisting of spacelike sheets, with temporal rules confined to the operators embedded in the sheets, suggests that its inter-operator (state-wise, ectosyntactic) level of structure be regarded as essentially spatial in character. Thus, where *space* denotes the external relationships among operators and *time* denotes their internal self-relationships, one might also think of L_S and L_O as corresponding approximately to time and space. (The correspondence is "approximate" because L_S and L_O are mutually inclusive, reflecting the logical coupling of space and time; L_O topologically contains (L_S, L_O)-structured operators, while the operators descriptively contain L_O.) Where space and time respectively correspond to information and a combination of generalized cognition and telic recursion, one may therefore conclude that the conspansive evolution of spacetime is an alternation of teleo-cognitive and informational phases cross-refined by telic recursion involving extended, trans-Markovian telonic relationships.

Although it contains the observable aspect of SCSPL, L_O may in principle contain hidden (inobservable) parameters implicated in nomological relationships and therefore relevant to physical state. I.e., in addition to the standard dynamical variables of physics, L_O may contain additional dynamical variables that cannot be directly observed, but only theoretically inferred on the basis of more or less general observations. For example, string theorists, M-theorists and others often conjecture that the universe may be floating in some sort of external embedding space, its relationship to which yields explanatory value regarding the internal state or condition of the universe itself. SCSPL conspansive duality suggests that the putative "externality" of such a space is not a meaningful property; if such a space exists and is sufficiently relevant to the universe in which we live to be of explanatory value to us, then it is by definition an ingredient of SCSPL syntax and can therefore be regarded as residing within SCSPL syntactic operators. In fact, this is a direct consequence of the Reality Principle.

Although it would be possible to go on at length, this paper is intended to present a general outline of the theory rather than an exhaustive development. In conjunction with the principles and features enumerated above, the given framework should suffice to characterize SCSPL on an introductory basis and distinguish it in flavor and content from other theories.

8 SCSPL as the Self-Excited Circuit

We are now in a position to draw a few parallels between Wheeler's vision of reality theory and the CTMU.

The **Self-Excited Circuit**, the informational logic loop through which physics engenders observer participation, which engenders information, which engenders physics, is a tight characterization of SCSPL . . . so tight that it would be difficult if not impossible to replace SCSPL with anything else and neither violate nor fall short of Wheeler's description. SCSPL is logical in construction, has a loop-like dynamic, and creates information and syntax, including the laws of physics, through telic recursion generated by agent-level syntactic operators whose acts of observer-participation are essential to the self-configuration of the **Participatory Universe**. These acts are linked by telic recursion to the generalized cognitive-perceptual interactions of quantum-level syntactic operators, the minimal events comprising the fabric of spacetime.

Through telic feedback, state and syntax are cross-refined from unbound telesis or UBT, a zero-information domain of ontological potential, under the guidance of a higher-order law called the Telic Principle . . . a protean **Law Without Law** through which order is extracted from disorder as laws are configured according to the generalized utility of state-syntax relationships for agent-level operators or observer-participants. The binary yes-or-no indications prescribed by **It from Bit** are demanded by infocognitive monism and the fundamental status of two-valued sentential logic in SCSPL syntax. The world is not merely a cybernetic monstrosity, a "giant machine ruled by preestablished law", but a metacybernetic system with logical priority over machines and the laws they obey.

How come existence? is answered by the fact that the universe is a global SCSPL operator amounting to one vast, self-selective, self-expressive act of reflexive observer-participation, while **How come the quantum?** is answered by the hological self-replication of the universe in each one of its microscopic syntactic operators and agent-level telors. **Many observer-participants** yield **one coherent world** because, through MU, the universe relates to its contents as a homogeneous distributed syntax that syndiffeonically supports and expresses their distinctions even as they help it evolve through observer-participation and telic recursion. Individual solipsism becomes *distributed solipsism* through the mutual absorption of SCSPL syntactic operators, made possible by a combination of distributed SCSPL syntax and shared teleology.

The Reality Principle, along with MAP, M=R and other logical guarantors of cosmic self-containment, shows that the syntactic stability of reality rules out any infinite reptilian regress of **turtle on turtle**, while the familiar **continuum** of classical physics corresponds to a syntactic (LMS) interpolation of the conspansive manifold generated by discrete SCSPL grammatical operations. Where **space and time** correspond to *information* and *generalized cognition* respectively, and where information and cognition are logically entwined in infocognitive SCSPL syntactic operators intersecting in states and state-transition events, space and time are entwined in a conspansive event-lattice connected by syntax and evolving through mutual absorption events among syntactic operators, symmetric instances of generalized observation influenced by telic recursion. Thus, time is not "fed into" the explanation of existence, but is a function of conspansive, telic-recursive SCSPL grammar.

The ultimate **boundary of the boundary** of the universe is UBT, a realm of zero constraint and infinite possibility where neither boundary nor content exists. The supertautologically-closed universe buys internal diffeonesis only at the price of global synesis, purchasing its informational distinctions only at the price of coherence. **No question? No answer!** reflects the fact that reality consists not of mere information, but *infocognition*, and that information on state is crucially linked to and dependent on syntax . . . the syntax of the "questions" asked of itself by the self-configuring universe. Due to the self-configurative freedom inherited by reality from UBT, the dynamically self-configuring universe displays uncertainty and complementarity and thus cannot be locked into locally-determinate answers for all possible questions at once, while the extended self-connectivity of conspansive spacetime unavoidably implicates the environment in the Q&A.

The **Super-Copernican Principle** reflects the distribution of the creation event over every point of spacetime according to the Extended Superposition Principle, which describes the way consequent states and events are atemporally superposed in their antecedent states and events. **Generalized consciousness**, the unitary reflexivity of the universe, is a fair description of the self-configuration and self-processing capacity of SCSPL as captured by the Telic and M=R Principles, while conspansive spacetime links spatially and temporally distant objects in a web of contact and communication exceeding even the neural connectivity of a human brain. And the CTMU describes the universe as just the sort of complex, teleologically self-variegating, self-synthesized information system prescribed by **More is different**, telic-recursively explicating multiplicity and diffeonesis from the unity and synesis of distributed SCSPL syntax, the (unique) CTMU counterpart of what has sometimes been called "the Implicate Order".[23]

The above analogy is only partial, and it is nowhere implied that the current presentation is without its gaps. But in fairness, several crucial points can be made in favor of the CTMU even at this early stage of exposition. First, it is supertautological; being

---

[23] The Implicate Order is a concept championed by the late physicist David Bohm in connection with his interpretation of quantum mechanics. Using the analogy of a hologram, Bohm proposed a species of self-similarity whereby "everything is enfolded into everything". According to Bohm, this "implicate order" is complementary to an "explicate order", the result of unfolding it through a process called the "holomovement". This bears mention because of its superficial resemblance to the conspansive unfolding of state from syntax in SCSPL, which displays its own version of logical hyperconnectivity, and the similarity between hology and holography. However, since the CTMU intersects only partially with Bohm's theory, the analogy should not be overextended.

---

constructed to mirror logical tautology up to the level of model theory and beyond, it is true in much the same way that a theory of pure mathematics would be true, but with reference to an expanded universe consisting of both mathematical and physical reality. Indeed, the CTMU can be viewed as a theory of the mathematical structure of a new mathematical object, SCSPL. Second, it has considerably more explanatory scope than other theories, providing a framework that is capable of accommodating the logic of self-determinative cosmogony without prejudicially excluding (e.g.) subjective and non-material aspects of reality. Third, it largely embeds current models of reality, at least to the extent that these models have not already been pushed beyond their explanatory capacities. And fourth, it has what appear to be empirically valid implications absent from other theories except as assumptions or unexpected observations, e.g. accelerating cosmic expansion. But perhaps the most important thing at this point is that in principle, any apparent explanatory gaps can be filled. That is, if something can be explained within the realm of standard science, then it can be even better explained in an inclusive model fortified with conspansive duality.

The ramifications of the CTMU are sufficiently extensive that their issuance from a single theory almost demands an explanation of its own. The scientific, mathematical and philosophical implications of the CTMU are many and varied, running the gamut from basic physics and cosmology to evolutionary biology, the theory of cognition, the foundations of mathematics and the philosophies of language and consciousness. But to be fair, nothing less is to be expected of a true "reality theory", particularly one that takes the form of a description of the relationship between mind and the universe. After all, the CTMU is so-named because it is a symmetric cross-interpretation of mental and physical reality, logically mapping the concrete universe into an abstract theory of generalized cognition and vice versa according to the M=R Principle. Were its implications anything less than profound, it would be miscategorized and misnamed.

The CTMU says that reality is a language . . . a self-explanatory, self-theorizing, self-modeling structure identical to its universe. As such, it can be regarded as a limit or "contraction" of model theory in which theory and universe coincide on the syntactic level of theoretical structure. Whereas most scientific theories are hopefully mapped into or onto the universe across an unbridgeable dualistic gulf, the CTMU is a monic theory of perception that simply eliminates the gulf by tautologically injecting logic in its entirety, including logical extensions of model theory and the logic of formalized theories, into reality as distributed self-transductive syntax. The CTMU is able to do this because it is a hard mathematical fact that anything which does not conform to the syntax of logic is inconsistent and therefore not a part of any stable, coherent reality. Because the reality we inhabit is visibly stable and coherent, the correctness of this move is assured. By eliminating the theory-universe gulf on the level of cognitive and perceptual syntax, the CTMU admirably fulfills the criterion of theoretic economy . . . and supertautologically at that.

Does the CTMU qualify as a realization of Wheeler's vision, and is it alone in this distinction? While one naturally hesitates to put words into the mouth of an icon, one or both of two things seems to be true: either relatively few reality theorists are inclined to share Wheeler's far-reaching worldview, or relatively few reality theorists are able to understand this worldview and pursue its implications. Consequently, despite Wheeler's eminence as a physicist, his has almost seemed a voice in the wilderness, leaving some with the impression that his deepest speculations have more the ring of distant prophecy than immediate theoretical practicality. But while the questions, "no's" and clues in terms of which Wheeler describes his vision may occasionally appear heavier on intuition and creativity than on logical and mathematical rigor, they are just the sort of intuitive distillations of mathematical insight that one might expect from one so experienced in logical and quantitative reasoning. In conjunction with other necessary principles, they can be transformed into logico-mathematical properties of reality with enough restrictive power among them to determine a new mathematical structure called SCSPL, the ultimate "intrinsic language". When all is said and done, there are excellent reasons to believe that this structure is unique, and that any additional principles that Professor Wheeler might have in mind can be accommodated by the CTMU as surely as by logic itself.

9 The CTMU and Intelligent Design

Design theory, which traces its origins to traditional theological "arguments from design" holding that nature was more or less obviously designed by a preexisting intelligence, maintains that the observed complexity of biological structures implies the involvement of empirically detectable intelligent causes in nature. *Intelligent Design*, the most recent scientific outgrowth of Design Theory, is a scientific research program based on a more philosophically neutral, and therefore scientific, search for instances of a clear, objective, standard form of biological complexity. According to William Dembski (1997), one of the movement's leading spokesmen, this has led to "a theory of biological origins and development" according to which "intelligent [and empirically detectable] causes are necessary to explain the complex, information-rich structures of biology." In view of the informational nature of complexity, Dembski observes that "information is not reducible to natural causes . . . the origin of information is best sought in intelligent causes. Intelligent design thereby becomes a theory for detecting and measuring information, explaining its origin, and tracing its flow."

One of the first things to note about the above definition is that it couples the implied definitions of *intelligence, causation* and *information* to a greater extent than do most dictionaries, pointing in principle to a joint definition of all of them. Since any good definition requires a model, one might be strongly tempted to infer on this basis that ID, as here defined, has a well-defined model in which all of its constituent concepts are related. It may therefore come as a surprise to many that perhaps the most frequent, or at any rate the most general, objection to ID in the wider intellectual community is that it "has no model". According to its critics, it lacks any real-world interpretation specifying a fundamental medium able to support it or a means by which to realize it.

Furthermore, its critics claim, its central hypothesis is not only beyond proof, but unrealistic and not amenable to empirical confirmation.

In all fairness, it must be noted that insofar as science has itself spectacularly failed to agree on a global model of reality, this is really nothing more than an exercise in hypocrisy. Science observes, relates and extrapolates from observations with what often turns out to be great efficiency, but has time and time again proven unable to completely justify its reductions or the correspondences between its theories and the real universe as a whole. Although some critics claim that beyond a certain point, explanation is pointless and futile, they do not speak for science; the entire purpose of science is explanation, not rationally unsubstantiated assertions to the effect that a closed-form explanation is "unavailable" or "unnecessary". In seeking a coherent explanation for existence – an explanation incorporating an ontological design phase that is rational, coherent and therefore intelligent – the ID program is in fact perfectly consistent with science.

However, being perfectly consistent with science means merely that something is in line for a model, not that it already has one. It has thus been possible for dedicated critics of ID to create the illusion, at least for sympathetic audiences, that they have it at a critical disadvantage. They contend that while science must be instrumental to society, yield specific predictions, and thus cite specific structural and dynamical laws that nontrivially explain its contexts of application, ID is nothing more than a Trojan horse for religious ideology, makes no nontrivial predictions, and is devoid of theoretical structure. Due to the number of sympathetic ears that such claims have found in Academia, this illusion has all but promoted itself to the status of a self-reinforcing mass delusion in certain closed-minded sectors of the intellectual community. Obviously, it would be to the advantage of the ID movement, and society as a whole, to end this contagion by putting forth something clearly recognizable as a model.

The problem, of course, is that as long as science in general lacks a fundamental model, so do all particular strains of science *including* Intelligent Design. Due to the close connection between fundamentality and generality, ID or any other field of scientific inquiry would ultimately have to provide *science in general* with a fundamental model in order to provide one for itself. This might have led some people, in particular those who doubt the existence of a stable fundamental model of reality, to suppose that the ID controversy would remain strictly within the realm of philosophy until the end of time. But this is not the case, for if there were really no fundamental model – if there were no way to map theoretic cognition onto reality *in its entirety* – perception itself would lack a stable foundation. Perception, after all, can be described as the modeling of objective reality in cognition, and the modeling of cognition in objective reality. The self-evident perceptual stability of reality, on which the existence and efficacy of science and scientific methodology absolutely depend, bear unshakable testimony to the existence of a fundamental model of the real universe.

The general nature of this model can be glimpsed merely by considering the tautological reflexivity of the term "self-evident". Anything that is self evident *proves* (or *evidences*) *itself*, and any construct that is implicated in its own proof is tautological. Indeed, insofar as observers are real, perception amounts to reality tautologically perceiving itself. The logical ramifications of this statement are developed in the super-tautological CTMU, according to which the model in question coincides logically and geometrically, syntactically and informationally, with the process of generating the model, i.e. with generalized cognition and perception. Information thus coincides with information transduction, and reality is a tautological self-interpretative process evolving through SCSPL grammar.

The CTMU has a meta-Darwinian message: the universe evolves by hological self-replication and self-selection. Furthermore, because the universe is natural, its self-selection amounts to a cosmic form of *natural* selection. But by the nature of this selection process, it also bears description as *intelligent self-design* (the universe is "intelligent" because this is precisely what it must be in order to solve the problem of self-selection, the master-problem in terms of which all lesser problems are necessarily formulated). This is unsurprising, for intelligence itself is a natural phenomenon that could never have emerged in humans and animals were it not already a latent property of the medium of emergence. An object does not displace its medium, but embodies it and thus serves as an expression of its underlying syntactic properties. What is far more surprising, and far more disappointing, is the ideological conflict to which this has led. It seems that one group likes the term "intelligent" but is indifferent or hostile to the term "natural", while the other likes "natural" but abhors "intelligent". In some strange way, the whole controversy seems to hinge on terminology.

Of course, it can be credibly argued that the argument actually goes far deeper than semantics . . . that there are substantive differences between the two positions. For example, some proponents of the radical Darwinian version of natural selection insist on randomness rather than design as an explanation for how new mutations are generated prior to the restrictive action of natural selection itself. But this is untenable, for in any traditional scientific context, "randomness" is synonymous with "indeterminacy" or "acausality", and when all is said and done, acausality means just what it always has: *magic.* That is, something which exists without external or intrinsic cause has been selected for and brought into existence by nothing at all of a causal nature, and is thus the sort of something-from-nothing proposition favored, usually through voluntary suspension of disbelief, by frequenters of magic shows.

Inexplicably, some of those taking this position nevertheless accuse of magical thinking anyone proposing to introduce an element of teleological volition to fill the causal gap. Such parties might object that by "randomness", they mean not acausality but merely causal ignorance. However, if by taking this position they mean to belatedly invoke causality, then they are initiating a causal regress. Such a regress can take one of three forms: it can be infinite and open, it can terminate at a Prime Mover which itself has no causal explanation, or it can form some sort of closed cycle doubling as Prime Mover and that which is moved. But a Prime Mover has seemingly been ruled out by assumption, and an infinite open regress can be ruled out because its lack of a stable recursive syntax would make it impossible to form stable informational boundaries in terms of which to perceive and conceive of reality.

What about the cyclical solution? If one uses laws to explain states, then one is obliged to explain the laws themselves. Standard scientific methodology requires that natural laws be defined on observations of state. If it is then claimed that all states are by definition caused by natural laws, then this constitutes a circularity necessarily devolving to a mutual definition of law and state. If it is then objected that this circularity characterizes only the *process* of science, but not the objective universe that science studies, and that laws in fact have absolute priority over states, then the laws themselves require an explanation by something *other than* state. But this would effectively rule out the only remaining alternative, namely the closed-cycle configuration, and we would again arrive at . . . magic.

It follows that the inherently subjective process of science cannot ultimately be separated from the objective universe; the universe must be self-defining by cross-refinement of syntax and state. This brings us back to the CTMU, which says that the universe and everything in it ultimately evolves by self-multiplexing and self-selection. In the CTMU, design and selection, generative and restrictive sides of the same coin, are dual concepts associated with the alternating stages of conspansion. The self-selection of reality is inextricably coupled to self-design, and it is this two-phase process that results in *nature*. Biological evolution is simply a reflection of the evolution of reality itself, a process of telic recursion mirroring that of the universe as a whole. Thus, when computations of evolutionary probability are regressively extrapolated to the distributed instant of creation, they inevitably arrive at a logical and therefore meaningful foundation.

The CTMU says that on logical grounds, reality has generative and restrictive phases, and that evolution has generative and restrictive phases that are necessarily expressed in terms of those of reality. It asserts that the meta-cybernetic mechanism of evolution is telic recursion, an atemporal process which sets up a stratified dialectic between syntax and state, organism and environment, with mutually consistent mutable and invariant levels. It says that this process, though subject to various forms of noise, interference and competition predicated on the internal freedom of reality, tends to maximize the utility of the universe and its inhabitants. And it thus says that evolution is much more than a mere environmental dictatorship in which inexplicable laws of nature call the tune as biology slavishly dances the jig of life and death.

The CTMU says that by its self-generative, self-selective nature, which follows directly from the analytic requirement of self-containment, reality is its own "designer". Other features of the generative grammar of reality imply that reality possesses certain logical properties traditionally regarded as theological or spiritual, and that to this extent, the self-designing aspect of reality is open to a theological or spiritual interpretation. The CTMU, being a logical theory, does not attempt to force such an interpretation down anyone's throat; not all semantic permutations need affect theoretical structure. What it does do, however, is render any anti-theological interpretation *a priori* false, and ensures that whatever interpretation one chooses accommodates the existence of an "intelligent designer" . . . namely, reality itself. In light of the CTMU, this is now a matter more of logic than of taste.

In any case, it should be clear that the CTMU yields new ways of looking at both evolution and teleology. Just as it is distinguished from other theories of cosmic evolution by its level of self-containment, particularly with regard to its preference for self-determinacy rather than external determinacy or indeterminacy, so for its approach to biological evolution. Unlike other theories, the CTMU places evolutionary biology squarely in the context of a fundamental, self-contained model of reality, thus furnishing it with an explanation and foundation of its own instead of irresponsibly passing the explanatory buck to some future reduction; instead of counting it sufficient to model its evolutionary implications in the biological world, the CTMU establishes model-theoretic symmetry by providing a seamless blend of theory and universe in which the biological world can itself be "modeled" by physical embedment. This alone entitles it to a place in the evolutionary debate.

Acknowledgments

The author wishes to thank Gina Lynne LoSasso for creating the diagrams that appear in this paper and for many stimulating discussions and feedback regarding the presentation of this work. Many thanks are also in order for a number of individuals who have supported and followed my work and contributed stimulating questions that helped me to explicate the CTMU in its current level of detail. These include, among others, Robert North Seitz, John Chapman, Angell O. de la Sierra, Mike Doyle, Phillip Hopp, Quinn Tyler Jackson, Evangelos Katsiolis, Paul Kisak and Anthony Nolan.

Acknowledgments

References

Behe M. J. (1998) *Darwin's Black Box: The Biochemical Challenge to Evolution.* New York: Simon & Schuster.

Berlinski, D. (2001) What Brings a World into Being? *Commentary,* Vol. 111, No. 4, p. 17. Online edition: https://www.commentarymagazine.com/articles/david-berlinski/what-brings-a-world-into-being/

Dembski A. W. (1997) Intelligent Design as a Theory of Information. *Perspectives on Science and Christian Faith,* Vol. 49, No. 3, pp. 180-190. Available at https://www.asa3.org/ASA/PSCF/1997/PSCF9-97Dembski.html and https://www.discovery.org/a/118/

Dembski W. A. (1998) *The Design Inference: Eliminating Chance through Small Probabilities.* Cambridge: Cambridge University Press.

Eddington, A. (1933) *The Expanding Universe.* Cambridge: Cambridge University Press. Available online at https://archive.org/details/in.ernet.dli.2015.220736/page/n7/mode/2up

Gellert, W., Kustner, H., Hellwich, M., Kastner, H. (Eds.) (1977) *The VNR Concise Encyclopedia of Mathematics.* New York: Van Nostrand Reinhold Company.

Gödel, K. (1962) *On Formally Undecidable Propositions of Principia Mathematica and Related Systems.* Translated by B. Meltzer. New York: Basic Books.

Langan, C. M. (1999) Introduction to the CTMU. *Ubiquity,* Vol. 1, No. 1. Also available at https://web.archive.org/web/20000603133703/http://www.megafoundation.org/CTMU.html

Langan, C. M. (2001a) Physics and Metaphysics. *Noesis-E,* Vol. 1, No. 3. Also available at https://web.archive.org/web/20180804031832/http://www.megafoundation.org/CTMU/Articles/Supernova.html

Langan, C. M. (2001b) Of Trees, Quads, and God. *Noesis-E,* Vol. 1, No. 4.

Langan, C. M. (2002a) *The Art of Knowing: Expositions on Free Will and Selected Essays.* Eastport, NY: Mega Foundation Press.

Langan, C. M. (2002b) The Theory of Theories. *Noesis-E,* Vol. 2, No. 1. Also available at https://web.archive.org/web/20070207053049/megafoundation.org/CTMU/Articles/Theory.html

Russell, B. (1979) *History of Western Philosophy.* London: Unwin Paperbacks.

Shannon, C. E. (1948) A Mathematical Theory of Communication. *Bell System Technical Journal,* Vol. XXVII, No. 3, pp. 379-423 and 623-656. Retrieved from https://archive.org/details/bellsystemtechni27amerrich/page/n5/mode/2up

Wheeler, J. A. (1979) From the Big Bang to the Big Crunch. *Cosmic Search Magazine*, Vol. 1, Issue 4, pp. 2-8. Retrieved from http://www.bigear.org/vol1no4/wheeler.htm and http://www.bigear.org/CSMO/PDF/CS04/cs04p02.pdf

Wheeler, J. A. (1980) Beyond the Black Hole. In Woolf, H. (Ed.) *Some Strangeness in the Proportion : A Centennial Symposium to Celebrate the Achievements of Albert Einstein.* Addison-Wesley Educational Publishing Company, pp. 341-375. Retrieved from https://jawarchive.files.wordpress.com/2012/02/beyond-the-black-hole.pdf

Wheeler, J. A. (1990a) Information, Physics, Quantum: The Search for Links. In Zurek W. H. (Ed.) *Complexity, Entropy and the Physics of Information, SFI Studies in the Sciences of Complexity.* Addison-Wesley Educational Publishing Company, Vol. VIII, pp. 3-28.

Wheeler, J. A. (1990b) *A Journey into Gravity and Spacetime.* New York: Scientific American Library.

Wozniak, R. H. (1992) *Mind and Body: René Descartes to William James.* National Library of Medicine (U.S.), American Psychological Association. Retrieved from https://collections.nlm.nih.gov/ext/kirtasbse/9301710/PDF/9301710.pdf

Key Terms

Made in the USA
Monee, IL
08 November 2024

69634916R00056